15ª

A TIME TO KEEP

BOOKS BY PETER NEAGOË

Novels: EASTER SUN

THERE IS MY HEART

Short Stories: WINNING A WIFE

A Time To Keep

PETER NEAGOË

Coward-McCann, Inc.   *New York*

A TIME TO KEEP

CHAPTER 1

⊙⊙⊙⊙⊙⊙⊙⊙⊙⊙

"THE CRADLE OF OUR NATION IS THE VILLAGE," SAY
the Romanians, for the new blood comes from the village.
Teachers, lawyers, magistrates, physicians, statesmen come
from peasant stock.

Our village was in Transylvania, the region enclosed by
the Carpathian Mountains, which have the form of a
sickle, its point reaching at the north into Czechoslovakia,
the handle dipping southward into Yugoslavia.

It was considered a large village, having over five hundred homesteads and over three thousand souls. In many
of the homes three generations lived in peace and harmony, for the youngest generation was united to the oldest
by a common faith, the Christian, and a lore that the folk
preserved as their heritage of the ages. "From the beginning of the world," the peasants said.

About the beginning of the world they were clear. The
Bible gave it to them simply enough. It was when God
created it in six days, including Adam and Eve. And it
was very good, God said, in His infinite wisdom.

"While we do not live in Paradise, we have a beautiful

3

spot on the earth, and our burden is like that of Adam and Eve after they were chased out of the Garden of Eden because they ate of the forbidden fruit," the old people said.

The men earned their bread by the sweat of their brow and the women brought forth children, just like Eve. God had told Eve, "Thy desire shall be to thy husband and he shall rule over thee," and so it was with the women of the village.

The largest number of the population was Romanian, although at that time Transylvania was under Hungarian rule. But the Romanian peasant lived peacefully in his faith and the firm belief that the Great Ruler was God, His rule eternal, while that of the Hungarian was temporal and transitory.

Our village was purely Romanian; we had only one Hungarian there, Horvath the shoemaker, "one spear in the sheaf" as the peasants said, but Popa Radu, our priest, reduced it to half a spear because Horvath's wife was a Romanian peasant woman.

The village was situated on a plain, more than half of it surrounded by low hills beyond which rose the crest of higher hills and beyond them the summits of snow-clad mountains.

Most of the houses and barns had thatched roofs, many so old that weeds grew in them, and they looked like heavy fur caps seen from the tops of distant hills. And all the outside walls of the houses were whitewashed, but the one giving on the street had a sky-blue border at the base about two feet wide. And because most of the houses had only two windows to the street, they seemed from afar like blanched faces with unfathomable eyes "looking upon the world everlastingly," Uncle Gherasim said, adding,

4

"Our village, seen from the hills, is a delight to the eyes."

The peasants strove to make their life in the villages bearable with the help of their faith in a righteous last judgment, and by endeavoring to settle differences at home, that is in the village, with the aid of elders such as Uncle Gherasim, and if need be of their notary too.

Father was the notary, and having studied to be a lawyer he was considered a boon to our village, especially because he was devoted to the peasants whom he thoroughly understood. He was as much attached to the soil as they were, but when mother said he was a peasant at heart he pushed out his mustaches and humphed. Then he said, "Men like Uncle Gherasim and Andronic, the wheelwright, could make kings' councilors." With that mother agreed.

Old Gherasim was not my uncle, but everybody called him "Uncle" and all who knew him said he was "as wise as the serpent," to which Popa Radu added, "but not as gentle as the dove."

The three largest houses in our village were Popa Radu's, Uncle Gherasim's, and ours. All three were built of stone, had thick walls, and large vaulted cellars. The barns and stables were also built of stone and had tile roofs, like the houses. I was two years old when my parents moved to the village. It was spring. Swallows were building their nests under the eaves of the barn. Scores of them darted to the watering trough under which they found moist earth that they carried in their bills for their mason work. From the porch, where mother placed me on a rug, I watched the birds, clapping my hands with joy.

Nicodin, our manservant, caught one swallow in its nest and tied a red piece of woolen thread to its leg, making a

5

wide ring of it. Two summers in succession the bird returned to its nest, then it came no more. Irina, my sister, cried over this loss and I cried with her, although I had not missed "our friend," as Irina called the swallow. But then, she was five years older than I.

It was on the wide stone porch of our house where I first met Uncle Gherasim. He came to welcome us to our new home. He brought us a pot of honey of which he gave me a taste there and then, saying, "May your life be sweet and long, Peter."

"May the Lord hear your good words, Uncle Gherasim," mother must have answered, such being the custom and mother a paragon of propriety.

CHAPTER 2

∞∞∞∞∞∞∞∞∞∞

THE PILLARS OF OUR COMMUNITY WERE POPA RADU,
Uncle Gherasim, and Andronic, the wheelwright—three
sturdy pillars upon which more could have rested than the
burdens of our village, for, as Mayor Vultur said—he
was a younger man—they represented holiness, wisdom,
and shrewd gentleness. But after father came he was made
the fourth pillar. Popa Radu said, "It is true that we believe in trinity in holy matters, but in temporal let us have
it be four, like the wheels of a wagon, for we do not only
support a load but carry it." And so father was the fourth
wheel. He represented—Vultur said—the law. But Uncle
Gherasim countered that it was not so. Father was a coun-
selor, not a judge, and therefore more useful.

Uncle Gherasim was rich for a peasant. He possessed
ten hectares of good, cultivated land, two vineyards, a plum
orchard with over three hundred trees, two oxen, two
horses, one cow, five hundred head of sheep, and twenty
beehives. He managed well with the help of Anton, who
was only ten years younger than Uncle Gherasim, "somewhere between fifty and what the Lord knows," Anton

7

said when he was asked his age. He was so devoted to Uncle Gherasim that he would put his hand in the fire for him, everybody said, and when one day Popa Radu asked him if he would indeed do so, Anton answered, "I would gladly, your reverence, if the flames were not big."

Popa Radu had tried during the years to get Anton away from Uncle Gherasim, partly because Anton was a good all-around farmer, but mostly to win a run against Uncle Gherasim in the cultivation of plums and grapevine grafting. Anton had learned much of this from Uncle Gherasim, who was a wizard at both.

Anton never changed his answer. "I am as close to Gherasim as the shirt on his back, your reverence. How could I leave him? I thank you for the honor of wanting me in your household."

Popa Radu had more land than Uncle Gherasim, had four oxen, two cows, five hundred sheep, a bull, and a stallion. He drew revenue from these two animals and was very proud to possess them. Uncle Gherasim himself admitted that Popa Radu's bull and stallion were of the finest breed. With all that, the priest considered Uncle Gherasim better to do than he himself in worldly possessions. "I have three thousand souls to look after, a wife and two daughters—girls are no asset—while you have yourself alone. The day and the night are your own, Gherasim, so you can take the last drop of fertility out of the soil in wheat," he protested.

Uncle Gherasim answered that he too had duties toward the villagers. Did he not sit in committees, was he not daily consulted about one thing or another by the younger men? As to the night being his own, well, would his reverence exchange places with him? "A widower's bed is cold, your reverence," he said.

What could Popa Radu say to that? A giant of a man he was, bursting with health and masculine vigor, and his wife, Priestess Porfira as the peasants called her, a flower of a woman. Tall, fair of skin, ever cheerful, handsome in form and features, in her mid-thirties, Porfira was Popa Radu's most cherished possession. But of course, what he envied Uncle Gherasim for was the wheat he grew. It was always better than his own. Larger spears, heavier kernels, and richer in gluten. How did the old fox achieve that, the priest wanted to know. Yet he would not ask Uncle Gherasim frankly, because he was a good husband-man himself and besides, he sought information from the Agricultural Experimental Station at Bucharest.

As for Uncle Gherasim, he very simply applied the method of selection. And this most thoroughly. Then too, he did spend some of his winter nights at this work. While Anton was sleeping on the hearth bed in the kitchen, his feet sticking out from under the blanket but warmed by the thick bed of embers, Uncle Gherasim sat at the huge table and selected the wheat for spring sowing, kernel by kernel. It was love's labor with him. And so, he reaped as he sowed.

Andronic, the wheelwright, was an artisan. He had little land, one vineyard, a plum orchard, and a sizable garden in the back of his house. The land he worked on shares, and took time from his craft only to harvest his plums and grapes, with the help of a cousin and his children. He lived alone in a house "large enough for ten persons," he said, for, having lost his wife in the early years of their marriage, he decided to spare himself from the shock and anguish of losing another loved one.

The gossips said he was too timid to woo again. His wife he had only half wooed, they said, she having bewitched him. But she was a beauty, they admitted, and died suddenly leaving the poor young husband stunned.

Andronic had nursed his grief in secret. To the eyes of the villagers he was not a sad man but the same as when his young wife sang at her work and he, Andronic, carved the wood in the shed at the back of the house.

When a friend would say, "It is a lonely life, Andronic," he would not sigh and nod his head sadly, but answer, "You do not lose what you love in your heart. And then, my work brightens my day." That was true. Andronic loved his work, and "What is nearer to a man, after his wife, than his work?" Uncle Gherasim used to say.

When we came to the village Andronic had been a widower thirty years. He was "climbing toward sixty," he told mother. A lean, large-boned man, with deep-set black eyes under heavy eyebrows, "eyes that can look into your heart," the people said. Possibly because of his keen eyes did Vultur, the mayor, call Andronic's gentleness shrewd. And also because Andronic never raised his voice at the communal meetings but spoke gently, like a kind parent, at the same time persisting, in that kindly manner, in the face of all opposition.

Generally the opposition came from Popa Radu, who, in his capacity of spiritual leader of the people, pretended to know better than Andronic the temporal needs of the peasants, and also because he was a choleric man. And he had a powerful voice too, a command of the peasant vernacular and of old folk sayings that he brought into play as so much armament and ammunition. When he tramped through the street to the communal house, as one going to battle, a venerable peasant, to whom such questioning was permitted, sometimes asked, "Where are you hurrying, reverence?" His answer was, "To our committee meeting and I am well armed."

Despite his being well armed, he more often lost than won against Andronic. But he was a good loser and would say, "Andronic, my opinion was exactly the same as yours, therefore I wanted to try you and see how well you could defend it."

"It is what I suspected, reverend father," Andronic would answer earnestly.

Into this triumvirate was father taken. He was the legal mind and a man of book learning, as the peasants would say. He considered it his due, for a notary is in a village almost as high a functionary as the prefect is in his district—besides, he is closer to the people than is the prefect, and better understands them and their needs. Nevertheless father was pleased because the three men were remarkable, each one in his way, and like himself had the welfare of the community at heart.

But father was a quick-tempered man and mother feared he would clash with Popa Radu, who flared up in anger very easily too. "We should live in the city. With your learning, dear, you would soon make a reputation as a lawyer," she said.

"Barbara, my place is where I can be of most use to our people," father answered. The truth is that he loved the soil as much as any peasant, and having given in to mother's urgings and left his job on the estate of a wealthy boyar—after a short period in the city of Sibiu as the best alternative—he chose the post of notary in this village.

11

CHAPTER 3

⊙⊙⊙⊙⊙⊙⊙⊙⊙⊙⊙

OUR VILLAGE BOASTED OF THE BEST POTTER IN THE whole district. Some said there was none better in the whole country. His name was Ion Tudor, nicknamed Americanu, the American, because with his young wife Raveca he had spent many years in America, where their first child Alexander was born. Ion sent money from America to his mother. A good manager, she saved a goodly part of this money. She worked the piece of land she had on shares with a neighbor. When the Tudors returned from America, their son Alexander was a lad twelve years old. They found everything well cared for, as if a man had managed instead of a woman. The house had a new roof of shingles, the fences were in good repair, and there was a cow, too, in the stable, besides the two goats about which the Tudors knew.

In America Ion Tudor worked in coal mines and in steel plants and his wife took in boarders. She was a strong woman, cheerful, and cooked wholesome food for the men. So they saved money. Ion cherished the hope of taking up his pottery when they returned home. Their son

12

was given colored clays to play with in kindergarten, and the teacher found he had a decided turn for "using his little hands" as Ion put it. And he encouraged the boy. When Alexander started in at grammar school Ion bought him paper for drawing, colored chalks, and clay too. The teachers remarked that Alexander had decided talent. He drew quite well, but he was especially good at modeling in clay.

When the Tudors returned to their native village, Ion lost no time. There was the shed where he had done the pottery, where his father had worked and taught him the craft. The kiln too, in the back of the barn, was in good shape, for Vara, his mother, had seen to it while her son was in America.

Ion resumed his work as if he had never been away from it. The fifteen years in America had not weaned him from the potter's wheel. The hard work in the mine and the steel plant had coarsened his hands, it was true, but had not weakened them. In two months Ion had a goodly quantity of glazed plates and jugs as fine as ever he had turned out so many years before.

His son Alexander was a big lad for his years. He would be an asset in the home, his grandmother said. He could take care of the garden, cut wood, milk the cow and the goats, and do many other chores which would be mere play to a strong, healthy boy. But all Alexander did, in his grandmother's estimation, was play with clay. And what most amazed her was that Ion, her son, a sensible, mature man, gave the clay to the boy and let him do with it what he pleased. A waste of time and a waste of good clay that should better be turned into jugs.

"It is a sin," the old woman said. "The boy is taking

13

childhood into manhood. Look at him. He is as tall as his father, and he plays all day long with clay."

"That's his gift, mother," Ion said. "He is not playing."

"If he is not playing then I am blind—God forbid," Vara said.

"You are not blind mother, thank God, but you do not understand this thing. The boy is an artist. His teachers in America told us. What he is doing is sculpture," Ion said.

"The teachers in America. What do they know about our life? If they were here to see how much work we have, they would not say, 'Alexander, play with clay like a good child of five.' They would tell him, 'Earn your bread by the sweat of your brow' as the Lord tells us," Vara said.

Ion could do no better than say that in time Alexander would earn more than his bread. Vara said she prayed to God she would see the day when Alexander could earn his bread with the toys he was making.

By the time we came to the village, Alexander was sixteen years old. He had a room built against his father's workshop, a sizable place with a skylight and a large stove to keep him warm in the winter, and there Alexander spent "God's good days" as Vara put it, modeling in clay and carving in wood. He had many pieces which Vara herself admired. A little grudgingly to be sure, but then, could she say that the creature there did not look exactly like their big tomcat? No! And the sow, lying on her side and six porkers suckling, their tails curled, all so lifelike one expected them to move any minute. Still, were all these any more than clever, very clever, toys? What Vara found more than a toy was a piece of carving, Saint George slaying the dragon. Indeed, that was wonderful. Horse,

14

dragon, Saint George, all carved out of one piece of cherrywood. And one more piece, a crucifix. There it was, the Savior on the cross, all whittled out of a piece of wood, the cross and the Savior, and even the crown of thorns. But against these two pieces worthy of a man's efforts, Alexander had scores of effigies of animals. What if the schoolteacher said they were wonderful? "Fine sculpture," he had said. "Sculpture! A name," Vara said.

One winter day—it was the winter when I started at school—Uncle Gherasim paid a visit to Ion the potter and asked to see Alexander's workshop.

"I heard about your son," he said as they walked in. He stopped in the center of the studio and looked around. "Well, Ion, this is a fine place. And the light coming straight from the sky," he said.

"Alexander learned about it in America. A studio, they call a place like this," Ion said.

"Indeed! Well, well! America," Uncle Gherasim said, examining the pieces of sculpture. Then he said, "The Lord bless us, Ion, this son of yours has golden hands. Yes indeed, yes, yes, yes, golden hands." He was looking at the crucifix. Then he talked about other things, but his eyes rested on the sculptures. It was Uncle Gherasim's way when he was about to drive a bargain. He liked the crucifix and meant to have it.

When Uncle Gherasim bought a horse or a cow at the fair, he would examine the animal carefully, ask the price, say a few words about cattle in general, then he would go off on other subjects. The scarcity of hay, for instance, the poor crops that year, the last election in the capital— if the party in power was not agreeable to the peasantry—

things that would lower the spirit of the vendor. But all the time he spoke his eyes would be on the animal he intended to buy.

Those who knew Uncle Gherasim well said he talked so much because he wanted time to appraise the worth of the merchandise.

"But this way of his, talking about depressing matters?"

"Well that, you see, that's his way and . . . Can you teach an old horse to canter?" Question answered with question, the best form in perplexity.

So, at Ion's, Uncle Gherasim kept on talking, his eyes fixed on the crucifix. This time he did not speak about the scarcity of this or that, but about the severity of the winter and of the city people's lack of consideration for the peasant, who, as everybody knows, was the foundation upon which the country rested. What would this so-called gentry do without the peasant? Does it know how much toil the peasant puts into a loaf of bread, say? The plowing, harrowing, sowing, cutting the wheat, threshing it, winnowing and carting it to the city? Certainly it does not. And little he cares too, the city man. He asks the baker for bread and eats it, without even crossing himself when he sits down to the table. So he spoke to Ion.

At length he turned to the crucifix. "Now, about the worth of this, in money or something that has money value in it, like grain or potatoes, something like that, what do you say, Ion? What would it be worth?" Uncle Gherasim said.

"How can I tell you, Uncle Gherasim? My son puts all his time in these things, often late into the night, he works and works. You had better speak to him."

16

"Best way indeed. Call him over, then," Uncle Gherasim said.

Alexander was nearly as tall as Uncle Gherasim. Though slender, his lean face and broad shoulders bespoke physical strength, energy, and endurance. His gray eyes, shaded by black lashes, lighted his tanned face.

Uncle Gherasim measured him from head to foot, his eyes traveling slowly down, up, then resting on the lad's face. He was leaning on his cane, shepherd fashion. After a long moment he said, "This piece here, lad, is the work of your hands. Now, I have a place on the wall, at the foot of my bed. There is a peg in the wall, a green jug hanging from it since we were married, my woman and I, the Lord rest her soul in eternal peace. Every morning when I open my eyes, there it is, green as oak leaves. But a jug is a jug, hanging on a white wall or standing on the kitchen floor. A useful thing, surely, but only a jug. Now then, I looked at this piece here, Christ on the cross. It is, in a way, my lad, like an icon for a Christian home. To be on a wall, to be seen all the time. So then, say that I would put it in the place of the jug. In the morning when I sit up in bed I would see it there. Crossing myself for the new day I would look at Christ, not at the green jug. This is, in two words, my lad, how I consider the matter. But the piece is the work of your hands and there is the point. The wall is mine; this is yours. To have it, I need come to an understanding with you. Your father does not know its worth, I do not know its worth, but you do. Now, my lad, you know my thought." Having said his two words, Uncle Gherasim waited for an answer.

Alexander considered a moment, then he said, "I put three months of work into it."

"Three months, eh," Uncle Gherasim repeated, turning to the Christ. "Well that is where we can start. Every day a full day of labor, like the peasant's, is that so?"

"Yes! Labor," Alexander said.

"Well, work is work, if book learning does not mix in, like with the notary for example. For such kind we have no measure. He writes a paper, hands it to me and says, 'Two kronen!' I can't say, 'Make it one, sir.' I have no measure for such work. But this here, this is just hand work, like Andronic's. Only it is not a wheel and it is not a yoke, it is what it is. Three months' labor. So then, say for example that instead of putting that time into carving the wood, you had worked for me on the land. I would owe you, my lad, one hundred and eighty kronen and you would have had your food. Put that at a hundred kronen for the three months. That makes it a total, counted in money, of two hundred and eighty kronen. What is a man to do? Numbers are faultless. Their face never changes. Two hundred and eighty is always and everywhere two hundred and eighty. I will pay you that much. Just payment for three months' work. The wood, we leave out the wood. I will give you another piece. Twice as big if you want."

"It is fair," Alexander said.

This is how Uncle Gherasim acquired a piece of art. The first Sunday after his acquisition Uncle Gherasim invited us to dinner. For this occasion he had Anutza, a widow who did his laundry, prepare the dinner. Generally Anton, his factotum, who grew up in Uncle Gherasim's service and was nearly his age, prepared their food. Uncle Gherasim said that Anton was the woman in the

18

house. "He can sew on a patch as neatly as Anutza," he told mother.

Uncle Gherasim had a big house. Excepting the kitchen, all the rooms had wood floors of wide boards as smooth as ice from wear and scrubbing with fine sand. The kitchen had an earthen floor and it smelled like smoked ham, for the ceiling rafters and the boards were black from the smoke of many years. Uncle Gherasim's grandmother, as a young woman, did the cooking in that kitchen, on the large hearth just as Anton was doing it now.

Uncle Gherasim took us in the room where he slept. The crucifix was on the wall at the foot of his bed.

"Please look at it," he said, nodding his head toward the cross. It is a sin to point a finger at a holy image.

"It is very beautiful," mother said. Father agreed.

"And there is the jug that hung on the peg where the cross is now," Uncle Gherasim said. The jug was on the bench near the window. He did not have the heart to degrade it so much as to put it on the floor or in the kitchen, he said.

"That lad has golden hands," he said again of Alexander.

Uncle Gherasim was proud of his possession and he certainly did a good turn to Alexander. He was the first person to buy the work of Alexander, and doubtless the first peasant in all the country to buy a genuine work of art. Father said that crucifix was genuine art.

Father could draw, too. He amused me with drawings of chickens, a goat, a pig, and once he drew a giraffe. This animal looked very much like our goat only it had a neck yards long. Of course I had never seen such a creature but I believed it must be a true image of the giraffe, since the chicken and the pig father drew were like a chicken and like a pig.

In the following spring we visited Alexander and he made a sketch of me. Father said it was splendid. Even I could see the likeness, but I resented that he gave me such a big head and a very thin neck. By then, Alexander's grandmother had developed quite a confidence in Alexander's ability to earn his bread. When she heard that Uncle Gherasim paid two hundred and eighty kronen for the Christ on the cross, she was dumfounded. But, at the supper table, she soon found her tongue. "It is very plain," she began saying. "These things are images. Saint George and the Christ on the cross are holy Christian images, like the icons. You should make such kinds, Alexander. As you see, they have value. And now that you have taken to hewing that piece of stone the miller gave you, I have a very good idea for you, my boy. Make a tombstone from it. It will be small, but large enough for an infant's grave. Just a cross. Maybe a wreath of roses on it, like the one we saw at the Italian stone cutter's. You were with us when your father, God preserve him in good health, ordered the tombstone for your grandfather. He earns good money and his is a trade. The Italian, I mean. I saw you look at the tools he was using." Vara talked and talked.

Raveca, Alexander's mother, saw good sense in the old woman's words. She kept nodding her head. Ion said nothing. He was watching his son, who smiled, then he frowned a little, but remained silent. When his grandmother had done advising him, he rose from the table, went to her, kissed her on both cheeks and said, "Grandmother, didn't you tell me that one cannot make a horse

from an ass?" And he ran out before Vara had found her
tongue.

"Ptew," she made, looking at the door, "how that boy
can abuse an old saying."

CHAPTER 4

⊙⊙⊙⊙⊙⊙⊙⊙⊙⊙

FATHER HAD AN ONLY SISTER, AUNT VERONICA. HER husband, Uncle Rusu was *protopope,* a degree in the Greek Catholic and Orthodox clergy between priest and bishop. He was a very quiet man, learned—father said—kind and generous. He was wealthy. They had a large stone house in the city of Abrud, much land, and vineyards. They had three menservants, a cook, and a maid.

Mother had great affection for Uncle Rusu, but she was not very fond of Aunt Veronica. She admired her, for she was handsome, energetic, and an amazon of a woman. I saw her and Uncle Rusu for the first time in the winter when I started going to school. I had never seen them until then because Aunt Veronica and father had had a quarrel years before. Now they were reconciled. Father was a little proud too that it was Aunt Veronica who took the first step toward "breaking the spell," as he put it. When her letter came announcing their visit to us, father read it twice to mother.

"You are glad too, Barbara dear?" he kept saying.

"I am! Truly I am, dear," mother answered.

22

Aunt Veronica came with her husband and one of the servants in a large sleigh drawn by four horses. And she drove them. It was nearly evening when we heard the bells in front of the house. Father rushed out to meet them and mother followed him. Irina and I were told to stay in the house. We heard a powerful voice say commandingly, "Rub them down well, Mihai," and in the same voice, "Good evening, brother. Hope we find you all well."

A moment later Aunt Veronica came into the house practically carrying mother, whom she held round the waist. Uncle Rusu and father followed them in. "And these are your children? What is your name, big head?" she asked me. Before I could mumble my name she picked me up and held me way above her head, laughing, "I like you. You will be a man someday," she said and set me down as if she were trying to plant me in the floor. "And you are his sister. Don't pout. Come and kiss me," she said to Irina. She bent down to be kissed. Irina touched her cheek with her lips. "Now you, big head," she said to me. I wanted to do as Irina had done but Aunt Veronica took my arms and twisted them around her neck. "Now," she said, and pressed her cold cheeks against my lips. I felt that our large room had suddenly got smaller. Aunt Veronica was a full head taller than mother. She was taller than her husband too. His first name was Andrei but we called him by his second name, Rusu. The peasants call their priests by the given name, Popa Nicolai, Popa Vasili, but a protopope they call by the second name.

At table, Uncle Rusu would start to tell a story—he was very fond of hunting and knew many tales about this sport—but he spoke very slowly and Aunt Veronica would finish the story for him. She had a pleasant, deep voice and laughed so heartily that even Irina laughed a little. When dinner was over we remained seated at the table but Aunt Veronica jumped up saying, "I must see how the horses are," and rushed out.

"Veronica, put on your coat," Uncle Rusu called after her. She made a backward motion with her hand and was gone.

"And it is so very cold out," mother said, concern in her voice. Uncle Rusu shook his head. "And when I go out she bundles me up so I can barely move," he said.

When she came back her sleeves were rolled above her elbows, the arms red from the cold. She rubbed them briskly and laughed at her husband, who looked at her reproachingly.

When mother sent us to bed Aunt Veronica kissed Irina, then she said, "Now you, big head." I walked over to her. "My name is Peter," I said timidly.

"Of course it is, big head," she said and pressed me against her.

On Sunday Uncle Gherasim was with us for dinner. It was very gay. Everybody was telling stories over which they laughed. Then they spoke about children.

"It is the poor who have the most children," mother said.

"That may be their blessing," Uncle Gherasim said, chuckling.

"Two blessings are enough for us," father said. Then he had me recite a poem.

Aunt Veronica crushed me against her big chest. Her eyes were bright with tears that formed two beads in the corners of each eye.

24

Uncle Gherasim ventured to ask if they had children too. Aunt Veronica pushed me away, held me at arm's length. Without taking her eyes from me she said, "My husband has much holiness in him. That may be our blessing." She spanked me gently and lifted me on my chair. Mother was blushing and Uncle Rusu fidgeted with the cross on his chest. His pale face was bright with a gentle smile. He was looking at Aunt Veronica. In a moment she jumped up, went over to him and kissed him on top of his head. Mother smiled but tears were streaming from her eyes.

They stayed with us seven days. When they left I loved Aunt Veronica. I loved Uncle Rusu too, but it was a different love. There was a little sadness in it as in the love I had for our nightingale when we found it dead in its cage.

At parting, Aunt Veronica insisted we visit them the next summer and Uncle Rusu said in his gentle way, "Indeed, my dears, you must come."

So, in the following summer, father, Irina, and I set out on a journey to them. Mother said she could not leave home at this season when every day required her attention. "Veronica will understand," she said. She was right. Aunt Veronica did understand.

We were received like the prodigal son. It was, however, not a calf that was prepared for the feast, but a lamb. A whole lamb roasted on embers in the open. It was brought to the table on a huge plank with a rim so as to keep the juice of the meat in. And there were pancakes, several kinds of jams, fresh milk rolls, fresh cheeses, sour cream, and of course very good wines. And practically all the meals were feasts, but we only saw Aunt Veronica at table. She was everywhere save visiting with us. She told us, "This is your home now. Look after yourselves. I have no time."

Father said Aunt Veronica was meant to be a man but something had gone wrong at the last minute.

"She is a splendid woman," Uncle Rusu said. When he smiled his face lit up and became handsome. Uncle Rusu smiled when everybody laughed, but when Aunt Veronica was present and laughed, he laughed a little too. He seemed ever absorbed in meditation, yet he was prompt to answer when addressed. He was very polite and meticulous about his dress. Aunt Veronica was brusque, careless about her garments. But her hair was always neat. Very thick braids formed a crown on her head. In her brown hair copper-colored flames played when light fell on it.

We were very happy at Uncle Rusu's because we had the run of the big house and the courtyard. Uncle Rusu gave Irina a lamb. It was not a very young lamb but Irina succeeded in making it eat from her hand and follow her about. My pet was a young hunting dog named Nero. We played with our pets and they played together, only Nero was rough with the lamb. Irina scolded him, but he never learned better. He did not want to learn, she said.

Father spent much time reading under the large pergamuth pear tree in the yard. A millstone served for a table and a circle of benches around it for sitting.

Uncle Rusu had many books, some of which he kept locked in a cupboard. He gave the key to father as there were books father had never read. They were large and small books, all bound in leather, and a few had golden

26

clasps and corner pieces, like mother's prayer book. Father was very careful with these books. He spread a cloth on the table for them and we, Irina and I, were not allowed to touch them. I did like to look at them and was so attracted by the covers that one day, when Uncle Rusu came out of the house with two of these books in his hand, I asked permission to touch one. He smiled and allowed me to pat both of them.

In our home a book was a treasure. To me it was a thing full of mysterious wonders, and the key to them right there on every page, in every line and letter. So, when Uncle Rusu allowed me to touch his prized volumes I felt closer to those hidden marvels.

In my fancies I decided I would have a library myself, in my mountain hide-out, where I would spend with books the time allowed me by the life of a Haiduc chieftain. Of course I would do farming too, just like a peasant, like Uncle Gherasim, for I loved the earth as much as father loved it, and I had all the time in the world for everything.

I knew the story of Bujor, the great Haiduc leader, who was an angel of kindness toward the poor and the whip of God toward the rich. Uncle Rusu was rich and these books tempted me greatly, yet I told myself I would not steal them when I became a Haiduc but would come at night, when everybody was sleeping, and read them all, as father was reading them now. Then I would go to father and amaze him with my knowledge.

In the meanwhile I would keep this a secret from everybody. It was a good secret, therefore not a sin. Only bad secrets like stealing or lying were a sin to hide. Such must be confessed, preferably to someone you love, like a

27

mother, because it is easier. I believed then that it would not be too trying to confess to Uncle Rusu either because he was so kind.

I had all these and other fancies as I watched father reading under the pear tree. Maybe it was because I had such fancies father told everybody that my big head was not empty. He also said that I was a happy child. But then he did not know the great sorrows I suffered over the misfortunes of characters in stories Uncle Gherasim told me. How I cried, and even dreamed sad happenings and cried in my dreams.

Of course these sorrows did not last long, and at Uncle Rusu's I had none at all because nobody told me any sad stories. And in the summer it really is difficult to be sad. Everything is so beautiful and gay. Aunt Veronica was very much like summer.

I had never thought of it until one morning when we watched Aunt Veronica coming from the garden, and Irina whispered in my ear, "Would you like Aunt Veronica to be your mother?" It was a strange question and sudden too, yet a feeling came to me that I would like to have Aunt Veronica as a second mother. So I whispered, "Two mothers."

Everything was lovely until I disgraced myself. Fortunately this did not happen until two days before we left. On that day Aunt Veronica took us in the vineyards. The grapes were getting ripe, the early ones. One of these grapes was the Guarnesh, a large-grained white grape, all juice and so transparent the pits were visible. They seemed to swim in the sweet nectar.

There were many peach trees in the vineyard too, a late variety. The fruit was large and very beautiful. Wax color and pink to deep red, the peaches on the trees looked against the blue sky like spheres of precious stone on a huge blue tray. But Aunt Veronica warned us the peaches were not ripe yet. If we should find any on the ground we should first show them to her before eating. So I did not look for peaches, for I had tasted the Guarnesh grapes. I ate this marvelous grape, cluster after cluster. It was wonderful, having the freedom to pick whichever seemed to me the most luscious.

Aunt Veronica was making the rounds of the vineyard, inspecting the condition of the grapes to decide when some of the earlier variety should be harvested. We could not keep up with her nor were we supposed to. She had shown us a place where we should stay, Irina and I, until she returned. Several times she called, "Children, are you there?" We answered in chorus, "We are here, Aunt Veronica."

An hour or so before noon, Aunt Veronica came and we started for home in the small carriage that waited for us at the foot of the hill, the horse hitched to it and patiently standing in the shade of a large walnut tree. We had not gone far when the grapes suddenly played a nasty trick on me. I gave a little wail and a groan, but these did not cover the other noises which mortified me with shame.

I was sitting between Aunt Veronica and my sister on the driver's seat. Irina looked at me and covered her mouth. She burst out laughing.

"Now then, big head," Aunt Veronica said. She stopped the horse. I started to cry. Aunt Veronica wanted to take me off the carriage but I begged her not to. She patted my head and drove on. Irina pulled away from me. She was laughing crazily. When we got to the stream, Aunt Veronica drove the horse to the bank below the bridge and jumped out. Before I could protest she lifted me out of the seat and waded into the water up to her knees. There she put me in the water.

"Now big head, we shall have a little bath," Aunt Veronica said. I could hear Irina laughing in the carriage. Aunt Veronica turned around and motioned to her to be quiet. It did not help much. Then she quickly loosened my pants. "I will do it, please, Aunt Veronica," I said crying, but it was too late. In my shame I tried to squat down. The water reached to my neck. "They must come off, big head, the pants and the rest," Aunt Veronica said. Then I was naked. Aunt Veronica threw my clothes onto the bank and waded farther where the current was more rapid. Now she held me with my back against the current and plunged me in a dozen or more times, the water nearly up to my ears. Up and down I went. It would have been very pleasant had the awful shame not taken all pleasure out of me.

As Aunt Veronica lifted me out of the water after each plunging, she knew when I had enough of it. She said, "We are ready." And up I went in her powerful arms. She held me out so as not to drench her white blouse.

Irina told mother I looked like a big pink fish with a large black head being carried by Aunt Veronica from the stream. There was a thin blanket in the carriage. Aunt Veronica wrapped me in it and placed me beside her on the seat. And so we got home.

When father saw me bundled up like that he lifted one eyebrow as he always did when anything puzzled him.

"Here, take your son. We had a bath in the stream,"

30

Aunt Veronica said lifting me off the seat. Father carried me into the house, Irina trotting at his side jabbering what had happened.

"That's nothing, Peter," Uncle Rusu said after we had luncheon. "His High Holiness, the bishop, had the same thing happen to him. Those grapes are that way."

I did feel a little better, since they were amused then about His High Holiness, but the shame clung to me as Aunt Veronica's wet skirts had clung to her when we came out of the stream.

The remaining time at Aunt Veronica's I avoided Irina. When Nero played with her lamb, which had no name but which she called Lamby, I tried to stop him and did if he did not knock me down and escape. Aunt Veronica was very sweet to me in her brusque way. She told me about flowers and birds and even about the various kinds of work on the land. She spoke to me like to a grown person, never once asking if I understood what she was telling me. I really loved her. When she took me on her lap, not at all gently, I felt bigger than I really was and stronger too, as if her own great vitality were flowing into me. She smelled of the ripe fields. Never did she mention what had happened to me.

Uncle Rusu was very kind to me too in his gentle, shadowy way. Actually he did not seem quite real when Aunt Veronica was present, more like some saint that might any moment become ethereal and vanish altogether. But he had a very pleasant voice, not strong like father's, but mellow and warm like the deep notes of a cello. He sang for us beautiful folk songs. When he sang Aunt Veronica never took her eyes off him. She sat very straight in her chair, hands folded in her lap, as still as the Virgin on the icon that hung between the two windows of their large dining room.

When we left, Aunt Veronica and Uncle Rusu walked beside our carriage until we got into the street. They waved to us. They had invited us to come again in the fall when father and Uncle Rusu would go hunting the wild boar. I was happy with the anticipation of returning again.

CHAPTER 5

OOOOOOOOOOOO

IN THE AUTUMN WE WENT AGAIN TO AUNT VERONICA
and Uncle Rusu's. This time father insisted that mother
come with us. He said that Aunt Veronica would feel offended if she did not come. "You know she is very fond of
you," he said. That was true. But mother, so kind and
generous toward everybody, bestowed love on few people.
It was mainly her reserve, her modesty, which prevented
her from approaching a person whom she did not find at
the first meeting akin to her. It was so with Aunt Veronica.
Her great energy, her unending exuberance, her domi-
neering nature, were a shield against mother. She blinked
like a frightened child when Aunt Veronica pounced
upon her saying, "Barbara, you are a treasure of a wife.
My poor, saintly husband should have a wife like you."

This was the greeting Aunt Veronica gave mother when
we alighted from the carriage. And mother did not understand her. But as Uncle Rusu took her arm and said, "Do
you believe, dear Barbara, that I am not very happy with
Veronica?" mother understood him. He was happy. But
his love was a timid, humble, and worshipful love for

33

Aunt Veronica and his happiness was a quiet happiness with no high-crested waves, therefore without ripples also. For happiness is cut to the measure of a person's nature.

As to Aunt Veronica—was she happy? If to be alive in every fiber of one's being at every moment means to be happy, then she was happy in the extreme. But Aunt Veronica never gave happiness as such a thought. She merely lived to the full of her enormous vitality. When she was gay, all of herself was gay. When angry, every drop of blood in her was aflame. She was very seldom angry, Uncle Rusu vouched for that. "Twice only have I seen Veronica angry. And there was nothing anybody could do to calm her. Her passion had to spend itself like a sudden storm," he said.

This was Aunt Veronica. As a hostess, mother admitted readily, she was ideal. She gave us the house and never encumbered us with any other manifestation of hospitality. She went about her work and we did as we pleased. At meals she appeared, bringing a wholesome appetite with her. And all she said after Uncle Rusu had finished the prayer of thanks for the food, was, "Now, let us eat." She never had to call the servant for more of one thing or another. The table was laden with food and bottles of wine and mineral water. Uncle Rusu cut his wine with this water. We, Irina and I, had spring water with our wine and so had mother. Aunt Veronica and father took the wine undiluted. Every day was a holiday for us.

Father and Uncle Rusu had long discussions on religion. Father had started several times to criticize the clergy but mother, who always sat by, intervened and he, all flushed with resentment, had to change the subject.

In revenge he took issue with Uncle Rusu on certain texts
in the Bible. He had studied Hebrew with a Rabbi in
Poland during his military service. He said that the Hebrew text was incorrectly translated.

Uncle Rusu listened to him earnestly, "very patiently,"
mother said. When father had finished talking Uncle
Rusu would quote the passage in Greek, then in Hebrew,
and quietly reaffirm his contention.

Aunt Veronica was never present at those discussions.
She was everywhere but in the house. When she came in
she brought the freshness and autumn fragrance of the
fields. Uncle Rusu always stretched out his arms to her,
smiling. She would bear down on him, push his arms
away, and kiss him on the forehead. Then she would tell
briefly what work had been done by the men. Never did
she mention her part in it.

Then came the day of the boar hunt. Uncle Rusu, father, and several peasants set out before we were up. It
was a bright, cool autumn morning. Irina and I, soon after
breakfast, went into the orchard to gather the walnuts
that might have been missed on the ground by the pickers.
With Irina it was a game, but I felt that I was doing a
useful chore, helping Aunt Veronica. I was happy about
it.

At noon mother expressed her anxiety about the hunt-
ers. Aunt Veronica laughed and told her there was nothing to be concerned about. But father, mother told her,
had once had a frightful experience. He was to go wild-
boar hunting with some friends who disappointed him
at the last moment. They could not go that day. Father
took their dogs and went alone. He was in a beech forest.
The dogs had scattered. He heard them suddenly nearer.

35

They were on the prey. Then he saw a wild porker running toward him. He shot it. Then several dogs came leaping and behind them a big sow, followed by other dogs and four or five porkers. The wild animal made for father. He shot and missed. Having no time to reload his gun he took to flight. The enraged creature might have caught him if not for its young, which, harassed by the dogs, squealed and the mother charged the dogs instead. Yet even so, it was a ravine that saved father. Coming to it, he made a superhuman effort to jump across, and did so, falling on his face on the other edge of the cleft. He thought then that he was lost, for he was too exhausted to rise and resume his flight. Again the dogs played their part in saving him. As the enraged sow made to jump across, two dogs leaped at her. The three animals fell into the precipice. Father heard the agonized cry of the dogs. He rose from the ground and looked. The dogs were gored and the sow was still slashing their quivering bodies. Father loaded the gun and discharged both barrels into the wild sow.

Aunt Veronica's only comment was, "This brother of mine was always a great runner." She laughed. Mother's anxiety remained in her eyes. Then she said, "Veronica dear, I feel, really . . . I wish they were back."

"Now, Barbara! You have your premonitions, I know. But you know it is a habit with you, like those stains on your finger. Brother told me. You never have had your so-called premonitions verified," Aunt Veronica said. Then one of the men came to the door and called her. "Come! Come all of you and watch the men thresh the lentils," Aunt Veronica said. She rushed out.

Mother came out with us but she remained on the

porch, crocheting. Irina and I ran to the barn. The men were threshing the lentils with flails, and the dry stalks and pods crackled under them. The men stood in a circle beating the heap of lentils in the center. Then they would stop and one of them would lift the broken stalks and empty pods with a wooden fork. The next moment they would ply their flails to the reduced mound.

Aunt Veronica did not remain with us long. She went to see the prunes being washed for drying. Later we joined her at the well.

Then we heard the dogs and the men coming. We ran into the yard. Father opened the gate. The dogs rushed in, then four men carrying someone on a stretcher made of two poles, ropes, and thin branches. Mother leaned over the porch banister. She cried, "My God, what happened?"

The four men looked up at her. Father said, "Nothing serious, Barbara. Andrei broke his leg." Aunt Veronica came from the garden. She hastened to the stretcher. Uncle Rusu smiled a little, and said, "I broke my leg."

"Set him up here," Aunt Veronica said to the men, indicating the millstone table.

"Better have him taken in the house," father suggested.

"Set him here," Aunt Veronica said.

The men placed the stretcher gently on the table. "Which leg?" Aunt Veronica asked. "The right. Above the knee," Uncle Rusu said.

Aunt Veronica started to pull his trousers off. Uncle Rusu groaned, then he fainted.

"You should have cut the trouser leg, Veronica," father said sharply.

Aunt Veronica did not answer. In a few moments she

had Uncle Rusu half naked on the stretcher. Then she said to father, "You should have tied two sticks to his leg and kept it straight, but . . . bring a board and two or three pieces of lath." She ran into the house and soon came out tearing a long piece of linen cloth into strips. The servant girl followed her with a bowl and a jug of water.

"Not yet," Aunt Veronica said to the girl. There was a vinegar-soaked sponge in the bowl. The girl stood at the head of the stretcher, frightened and interested. Father came with the board and several pieces of lath. Aunt Veronica felt with her fingers for the fracture, then pressed the leg, with her palms, from sides and top. Uncle Rusu groaned feebly, but did not come out of his faint. "Now," Aunt Veronica said, reaching for the laths. She applied three against Uncle Rusu's bare leg and bandaged them tightly to the limb. Then she lifted the stiffened leg. "Put the board under," she said to father. In a few seconds she secured the board to the leg with strips of cloth. "Now," she said to the servant girl. The girl held the vinegar-soaked sponge to Uncle Rusu's nose. Aunt Veronica sprinkled his face with the cold water and patted his cheeks briskly with wet hands. Uncle Rusu opened his eyes. "It is done," Aunt Veronica said. She kissed him on the forehead, slapped both his cheeks gently, for her, and said, "You will walk again, Andrei. Take his reverence into the house." She lowered her voice as she pronounced his name.

Aunt Veronica watched the men lift the stretcher and go toward the house, then she turned and walked rapidly to the garden.

Mother asked Uncle Rusu if they should have the doctor. "No, no, Barbara dear. There is no doctor who could do better than Veronica. One of our horses broke its leg. She set the fracture and we have the horse still. No, Barbara dear, I need no doctor."

But in the morning of the following day, when Aunt Veronica and the servant girl brought Uncle Rusu to the breakfast table, mother clasped her hands in amazement and cried out, "Veronica dear, what are you doing?"

"Now, Barbara, do not get frightened, a broken limb is no sickness. Andrei is perfectly well. The fracture is mending by itself if it is not disturbed. And it would be cruel of us to confine him to a sickroom when he is so happy to be with us," Aunt Veronica said.

They placed Uncle Rusu in his armchair, his broken leg stretched out in front of him resting on another chair. He was pale but he smiled, assuring mother that "truly Barbara dear, Veronica knows best, and I do wish to be with you all."

Uncle Rusu spent his day sitting at the table and resting on the couch where Aunt Veronica and one of the servants placed him, and if he wished to be moved again while she was absent, Matei, the coachman, and father would move him.

Mother watched these operations with great anxiety, whispering to father to be very careful. For answer father merely frowned, which really meant "I know what I am doing, Barbara," his usual comment when mother tried to influence him one way or another.

The atmosphere in the house changed after Uncle Rusu's accident. While Aunt Veronica was in the house she dominated, and even the furniture seemed to be charged with a sort of life, because as Aunt Veronica

moved about, chairs slunk out of her way apparently un-
touched, and the larger pieces lost size when she brushed
rapidly by them.

Father, reading by the window, although not stirring
from the armchair, would change color, his face like a
field now in sunlight, now in shadow. And mother's hands
would take on speed at knitting, the needles clicking.

But directly after Aunt Veronica left the room and we
heard her rapid steps on the yard pavement, all became
quiet and relaxed. From then onward until she reap-
peared it was mother who ruled. Actually she gave no
orders, nor moved things about; all she did was to preserve the quiet left behind by Aunt Veronica.

We, Irina and I, were allowed to stay in the room as
long as we made no disturbance of any kind. We had to
speak in whispers. To mother, Uncle Rusu was a patient
who had to be spared from irritation. I did not choose
to stay in the room except when mother and Uncle Rusu
sang together. That was beautiful. They sang quietly, as
if for one another. Once Aunt Veronica burst into the
room while they were singing. She stopped at the door,
closed it carefully, and tiptoed to the window where father was sitting with the book open on his lap.

The fall of the evening always had an influence on me.
Possibly I inherited from mother this feeling for the period
of time when the day "dies away gently and evening is
born," as Uncle Gherasim said.

At Aunt Veronica's, as at home, mother greeted this
daily event standing or sitting by the window and wist-
fully looking out. And when it got dark enough for lighting the lamps she turned to us saying, "This day too is
gone, good evening," and we answered in chorus "good

evening." It was a ritual in our home to greet the evening when the lamp was lit.

Tired from the day's activity, Irina and I welcomed the rest while waiting for supper, as this space of time was the quietest. Even father was silent for a short time and we all came to life when the light awakened us from our "open-eyed" dreaming, as the peasants say.

Uncle Rusu said it was a beautiful habit and they would adopt it too. In our remaining days with them, he asked to light the candle himself so that he should be the one to greet the evening. But instead of saying "This day too is gone," he said "Thank God for this day that is gone; good evening."

If Aunt Veronica was present she answered with a twice-repeated greeting, pronounced very rapidly, but there was cheer in her voice and not haste. Then she would light the huge ceiling lamp herself and say once more "good evening." Aunt Veronica did not mean to make a game of it, only she did everything so heartily and joyously that it all seemed to be a play with her.

"Nothing is beyond her capacity, everything is in the palm of her hand to do as she pleases," Uncle Rusu said to mother.

Aunt Veronica was an excellent cook, but she would not spend her time at the kitchen stove. "When I grow old and too fat to move, then yes, I shall be a cook," she said. But every morning she gave most precise instructions to the cook about the various dishes.

The wild-boar steak was broiled on embers after it had been doused with spiced vinegar, exactly as Aunt Veronica had directed. It was the first time I tasted wild boar. It was a sweet, rather tough and stringy meat, father said,

41

because it was fresh. Boar meat should be well cured, he said. Mother would not eat it. She connected the accident of Uncle Rusu with the wild boar, although father told her Uncle Rusu broke his leg after the hunt.

CHAPTER 6

⊖⊖⊖⊖⊖⊖⊖⊖⊖⊖

WHEN WE LEFT, OUR CARRIAGE WAS LOADED WITH presents from Aunt Veronica and Uncle Rusu. There were two sacks of walnuts, a bag of lentils, a large basket of dried prunes, two beautiful frieze blankets, white, with long fleecy naps, a large bundle of lovely embroidered pillow cases, and two new fur coats, one for mother and one for father. Irina and I got a sheepskin coat each, such as peasants wear on holidays.

Uncle Rusu got well in good time. He wrote to us and Aunt Veronica added a few lines in a bold, large hand, closing with the words, "We expect you when the swallows return in the spring."

During the long winter the family spoke often of our visit with Aunt Veronica and Uncle Rusu, and I wished now and again when the longing for Aunt Veronica came to me that winter would pass more quickly.

We never saw Aunt Veronica again. She was killed in the first days of spring. She was driving the four-in-hand when they met two gypsies and their bear, on the road. The horses, fresh and lively from their winter rest, got

43

scared at the animal. They shied and took to a mad gallop. The light carriage swerved from one side of the road to the other. The man who was with Aunt Veronica kept crossing himself in his fright. Aunt Veronica shouted at him to jump out if he was so scared. "I did jump out when the carriage was at the margin of the road. Clear into a freshly plowed field," he told Uncle Rusu.

The man escaped with a dislocated shoulder and a broken arm, but Aunt Veronica was killed. The carriage struck a milestone, and both wheels on that side were shattered. The carriage turned over. In falling out under the carriage, Aunt Veronica's neck was broken. She died instantly the doctor said, but her body was badly bruised and torn, as she was dragged some distance under the wrecked vehicle.

Mother and father went to the funeral but we children were not allowed to go. Not having seen her dead and buried I could not realize that Aunt Veronica was no longer alive. Even when our parents spoke about her and I saw in their eyes tears which made me cry, I could not believe that I should never see Aunt Veronica again.

Even today, after so many years, I can still visualize Aunt Veronica, tall, strong, and aglow with vitality. I can hear her voice and great laughter, and I have never seen another woman like her. No wonder Uncle Rusu could not live long after he lost her. *I* have never lost Aunt Veronica.

In those days mother contributed a great deal to keeping her alive for me. She spoke about Aunt Veronica with admiration and warmth. And later, when the sorrow was losing its power because it was slowly being submerged into memory, and also because mother believed firmly in destiny, and that Aunt Veronica could not come to the end of her days except as she did, mother and father recalled humorous episodes of her life and would laugh a little. It made me happy listening to their reminiscences about a person I loved so dearly.

Uncle Rusu had two sisters and two brothers, all of them older than he. They had children and lived in different parts of the country. They did not visit Uncle Rusu because the sisters did not like Aunt Veronica, and the other women of the family, his brothers' wives, were snobbish city ladies who considered Aunt Veronica a savage.

So, when Uncle Rusu wrote to us the following year that he was unwell, mother had a consultation with father and two days later they went to him. Mother made elaborate preparations in our home. She gave minute instructions to Lina, a peasant woman who was to stay with us and take care of Irina and me and the home. Father told Nicodin about what work was most urgent, such as bringing a few loads of wood from the forest, cutting it up, and gathering in the dry beans. "About other things you know what to do," father said.

Lina was a widow. She had a small house on the outskirts of the village, which she left in the care of her fourteen-year-old daughter. "Anna can take care of the goat, and Nicolai is eight. He can take care of himself," she said. She was very serious when she cleaned the house, but in the kitchen she sang at the top of her voice. Evenings she made Maria and Nicodin sing with her and they forgot to send us to bed at the time mother had told her. So I always fell asleep on the hearth bench with my head in Lina's lap. But in exchange for this omission Lina fed us as if we needed stuffing like the poor geese

mother used to stuff to fatten them. I was always sorry
for the poor birds. Mother would take a handful of corn
moistened with water, open the bird's beak and stuff it
down its throat. The goose would get so fat after two or
three weeks that it could no longer waddle on its feet in
the cage. Yet mother, who had great pity for any suffering
animal, believed simply that the fate of a goose was to be
fattened by stuffing corn into it. She also thought that
pigs knew more than geese, for they fattened themselves.
All animals that were meant for food should be fat, mother
believed, because that proved they were healthy. In those
days, fat people were not worried about their condition.
They actually prided themselves with their rotundity
and were envied by the lean who simply consumed food
without showing it, the stout ones said. I was one of those
who ate—and ate well—without showing it. Still, I do
not believe mother would have approved Lina's feeding
us. After each meal I felt drowsy and heavy for an hour or
more under Lina's care. She had her own way of making
us overeat. "It is different with people who have to be
sparing with cream, with lard, eggs, and sugar, but here
there is plenty," she said to Maria. So she made pancakes
for us every day for dessert.

We had only one week of this because father came
home. He did away with the pancakes, much to Lina's
disappointment, for she liked pancakes more than smoked
sausage—her choice among all the meats. But he introduced the eternal soup, which he said was medicine.
When it was not chicken and noodle, it was chicken and
tomato soup, and once a week beef soup. This last could
be with vegetables only or noodles, too.

I liked soup but what I relished especially was the

boiled beef. This meat father taught me to eat with raw onion. Once I learned to like the raw onion I asked to have it with every kind of boiled meat.

The onion is really a wonderful vegetable. We had a pet rooster that I fed daily as much onion as he would eat. The fellow grew very big but he was too domesticated to hold his own against another big rooster we had. This one strutted about like a most decorated general, showing off his beautiful red crest and wattles, and his long sickle-shaped feathers that were the envy of the gendarme, Sergeant Mueller. He had cock's feathers in his hat, but those on our rooster's tail were much more gorgeous. He begged mother to save those feathers for him when the time came for us to eat the proud rooster.

But we ate first the one I had fed onions to. Well, the good creature rewarded me for the onions I had fed it. Its meat was as strongly onion tasting as the flesh of the English sailor was tobacco flavored, to the disgust of the cannibals.

Father and I were the only members of our household who ate and relished the meat of the onion-fed rooster. Even Nicodin found it too strong.

Mother remained with Uncle Rusu. Father said the doctors could not find what caused his ailment. In fact they found no sickness in him at all. Uncle Rusu was simply "melting away like a wax candle in the blazing sun," as the peasants say. He was not bedridden. He rose every morning at his usual hour—which was at sunrise— and attended to a few church matters. He did not have the strength, however, to officiate in church.

Every day, father told us, mother had to prepare for him dishes that Aunt Veronica liked best herself. When mother asked him if he had no choice of his own, Uncle Rusu said, "Barbara dear, with this food I feel closer to her."

He ate little even of this food, and mother had to help him to take at least as much as she believed would keep him alive. But Uncle Rusu did not wish to live, father said. Mother had her own ideas about it. "He will live," she said. "He is not old. He is forty-five and his hair not tinged with gray."

Mother could not know the depth of Uncle Rusu's sorrow. He never wept when he spoke about Aunt Veronica. On the contrary, he was at those moments cheerful in his quiet way. A smile was in his eyes, as when he greeted her coming into the house.

A studious man, he never touched his books, but read, over and over again, passages in the Bible that Aunt Veronica had preferred. And he gave father his two guns, his hunting jackets, and other things belonging to that favorite sport of his. "I shall never go hunting again. I shall never leave the house. Coming back to it and not finding Veronica would be . . . I do not want to think of it," he told father. He never went to her grave but gave instructions how it should be tended.

When the men came to consult him about some work, Uncle Rusu told them to do as they had done during the years Aunt Veronica directed them. They had been a long time with Uncle Rusu.

Mother's first letter was encouraging. "Uncle Rusu will get well," she wrote. "I make him eat and take a little of the old wine Veronica used to give him. We do not speak of her often. I tell him about ourselves, the children, and the people of our village. He listens politely, asks questions

48

now and again as if he were really interested, but I know where his thoughts are." Then she gave instructions for Lina and Maria. Her second letter was as hopeful as the first. In the third she wrote that the famous doctor, Lucatch, came. He was a friend of Uncle Rusu and Aunt Veronica. He had known Aunt Veronica as a girl and would have married her, but she loved Uncle Rusu who was handsome. Doctor Lucatch was homely, his face was pock marked. He remained a bachelor, devoting his time to study.

"He told me Andrei will not live," mother wrote, "but I do not believe him. I asked him what ailed Andrei and why this ailment was fatal. His answer was, 'You see, my dear, we doctors know something of the human body, but not of the soul. Andrei suffers in his soul.' I do not understand his answer. Do not like it either. And I do not believe him. But if it is Andrei's soul, then he should be able to help himself. And I will help him, too. I will pray for him. Am I right, dear? I believe I am right. Prayer is medicine for the soul." Then again she asked father to remind Lina of one thing and another.

The fourth letter was more hopeful than the second. "I spoke to Andrei about prayer. Told him I prayed for him. He said, 'Barbara dear, it is beautiful and very good of you to pray for me.' He prays too, of course; he is a clergyman. He seems happier than ever. There is a light in his eyes that warms my heart. He is a little thinner, but this wonderful light in his eyes is life. I know it."

Several letters that followed enlarged upon mother's amazement at this light in Uncle Rusu's eyes. She insisted it was life, life surging into him, but she wondered why his body was wasting away. "We walk in the garden. I urge

49

him, and he never declines. But I must let him rest often. When we come in he seems exhausted. He sits in his arm-chair quietly and watches me kneel before the icon. Each time after my prayer he says, 'Thank you, Barbara dear,' and smiles. There is another thing with him now that makes me wonder. A few days ago he dozed off sitting in his chair. He seemed to have stopped breathing. I went over and very gently laid my hand on his chest. I could barely feel his chest rise and fall. The merest move. His heart I could not feel at all. But when he opened his eyes he smiled. Then he said something that frightened me. He said, 'Barbara dear, I dreamed Veronica touched my breast very gently, and said, "Sleep, Andrei, sleep."' Do you think, dear, this is a premonition? I am so frightened. But I did not show Andrei I was."

Two days after this letter, one of their men, Aron, arrived. He came to fetch father. Mother had sent him.

Uncle Rusu was glad to see father. He said mother was an angel. "She helps me on my way," he told father. He did not say "on my way to recovery" as father expected. Then he told father there was time but since he had come—and how glad he was to see him—he wished to have his will drawn up. "I have many relatives," he said with a smile.

It was an elaborate document, father told us later, for Uncle Rusu forgot none of his relatives. He also remembered the men and women who worked for him. He made it specific that the house and all property be sold. The heirs were to get certain shares of the money. Mother was to have the golden cross and chain he wore and father the four horses that caused Aunt Veronica's death. All of Aunt Veronica's clothes and the furniture of her room, also her few pieces of jewelry and small trinkets, were to go to the church and be distributed by the priest and elders to the poor of the parish.

"This is my will and testament," Uncle Rusu set as the concluding words and signed it. Then he put it in an envelope made by folding a large sheet of paper, and sealed it with five seals of sealing wax, impressed with the clerical seal of his church. He asked father to give it in the care of the local district judge, a friend of Uncle Rusu's.

With this accomplished, Uncle Rusu felt "as if his work on earth had been finished," father said. He seemed content. He was always a small eater but now he would take only a glass of goat's milk in the morning for breakfast and another for his evening meal. At noon he ate a little solid food and drank a glass of wine with mineral water.

After supper he sat at table with father and mother, listening most of the time to them, who were trying to cheer him up as best they could. He was very feeble now but with each passing day he became more cheerful. That light in his eyes of which mother wrote seemed to live by its own virtue, ever undimmed. Then, one evening, a week after father's arrival, Uncle Rusu merely tasted the milk. He set down the glass and said, "My dears, I shall be with Veronica soon." And he started to sing a hymn, motioning to mother and father to join in. They sang with him. When they stopped singing, Uncle Rusu leaned back in his chair and closed his eyes. In a few moments he opened them. "Send for the priest, please," he said.

He received the holy communion at the table. He bade the priest be seated. For a long moment Uncle Rusu sat with his eyes closed. At length he opened them as one awaking from deep sleep. In almost a whisper he said,

51

"Give me the candle. Kindly put it in my hand." When he grasped the candle he sighed a few times, then he seemed to nod. Father caught the candle from his dropping arm. Uncle Rusu was dead.

For a long time my parents spoke about Uncle Rusu's beautiful passing away.

∞∞∞∞∞∞∞∞∞∞

CHAPTER 7

WE HAD NO USE FOR THE FOUR HORSES UNCLE RUSU
bequeathed to us. They were fine animals and Nicodin
wished to keep them. He loved all animals but the horse
was his favorite.

Father sold the horses and I got, for the first time, two
summer and two winter suits. Mother said that was ex-
travagant expenditure as I would outgrow them. It was
different with a winter coat. That was always too big
for me the first winter and too short the third, but this was
easily remedied. Mother saved every kind of material—
woolen and cotton stuffs. In the third winter Irina's coat
and mine would undergo a thorough alteration. A few
inches of stuff that matched the coat near enough would
be added to its length and the length of the sleeves, and
the coat would be as good as new, mother said.

The materials mother saved served well in the household economy. If the sleeves of my jacket developed holes
at the elbows, mother found the right pieces for patching
them up. The bottoms of my everyday pants always had
patches, since they became everyday pants after having

served one year for Sunday and holiday wear. Even father's work trousers had a number of patches on them. We considered this as natural as washing ourselves in the morning, but Irina only allowed her dress or coat to be patched "where you can't see it," she said. Under the armpits, for instance. But on her shoes she had to wear patches. Horvat, the Hungarian shoemaker, was an expert at this.

Horvat was not very tall but he had wide shoulders and the biggest hands I have ever.seen. His bony fingers were thick, with large joints, but it was his thumb that always amazed me. When he said *one* he detached the thumb from a clenched fist so suddenly it snapped up as if by a powerful spring. The number two he demonstrated by snapping the little finger detached. He used this form only when concerned with large monetary units, as a ten-kronen bill. Lesser amounts he merely named.

When father ordered new shoes for me, it was Horvat's thumb and little finger that indicated and set the price. My shoes were not hobnailed but Horvat made solid shoes indeed. The soles were nearly as thick as one of his fingers and the heels had small horseshoes attached to them that would have ruined our floors if I wore my street shoes in the house. For the house he made me slippers without heels that were as good as skates. When mother did not see me I would glide the whole length of the room.

Father used to say that mother was as thrifty as three Saxons. He told us the story of a Saxon who was carting a load of cheeses to the city market. He had a loaf of bread with him and several large onions. When he stopped at a roadside inn, the Saxon ate his bread and onions and smelled the cheese.

This was an utterly unfitting example, for mother was generous when it came to food, and generous toward whoever was in need. But she never wasted a thing. She said that everything must find its use as water finds its level. And she helped the process. She said that good economy was nothing but orderliness.

One day when father found his work trousers newly patched on top of the old patches that had worn through, he said, "Really Barbara, are we so poor? Look at this," and held up the trousers.

"No, dear, we are not poor at all, we only are not rich," mother said.

"And in case these new patches wear through?" father asked.

"If the rest holds out, I will patch them again," mother said simply.

"Until the bottoms of my pants will have as many layers of patches as a cabbage has leaves," father said.

"The rest of your trousers won't last so long," mother said. That closed the subject. Father put on his pants, grumbling a little, and went to work in the garden.

We are not poor at all, we only are not rich remained a byword with us. And it described exactly our condition. Mother really did make much of the little we possessed. When friends came from the city to visit us they got the impression we were quite well to do. We always had wine in the cellar and a well-stocked pantry. Our table, though not sumptuous, was abundant in wholesome food. And mother was an excellent cook. Even our fast-day meals were as palatable as any with meat. A purée of beans, lentils, or dry yellow peas was, as mother prepared it, most delicious. When the district judge tasted the

55

lentils the first time he said he could never have believed the lentil had such wonderful flavor.

The district judge was Hungarian and a chauvinist. For him to grant that a Romanian could prepare such food was the highest compliment. He considered the Romanians an inferior race. Father disliked him heartily. But he was a superior functionary and mother induced father to extend the hospitality of our home to him. She was ever thinking of benefiting father.

"It can't hurt, dear, to have such men think well of you," mother said.

"Because of your cooking! Barbara dear, why . . . why," father answered, too irritated to find words.

Mother used to say that father never knew how to cultivate influential people. He always judged the man, overlooking entirely his rank. In her simple way, mother understood that there was a game to be played, and a man with father's mind and knowledge should be a master at it.

"But, Barbara, I am not a politician," father objected angrily.

"And what is a politician? Something superior? That is why I say it should be mere play for you to cope with politicians," mother said.

"It is not coping with them, Barbara. It is as you just said, play their game," father said.

"And what is to play their game? Simply let them believe what they say they believe," mother said.

"And what should I believe, Barbara dear?" father asked.

"You know what to believe," mother said, with a chuckle.

56

"And keep it to myself?" father said, amazed.

"Why not? Must everybody know your mind?" mother said as one who discovered something quite important.

"But, Barbara dear, we live by what we believe. We—" father started to say. Mother cut in elatedly, "That is exactly what I mean. We live by what we believe and it is nobody's business what our belief is."

"It is our secret," father said and burst out laughing. Mother was not daunted in the least. She laughed with him and then said, "You are always right, dear. It is our secret."

What could father do? He knew very well that in any case mother would have the last word, so he did not press the discussion further.

One time he told mother that she had absolutely no political convictions. Mother smiled sweetly and said, "How little you know me, dear, in this regard. I have every kind of political conviction." Father simply raised his right eyebrow, utterly nonplussed.

In those days the most influential Romanian daily paper in Transylvania was *Tribuna*. The editor-in-chief was Silvestru Arin, father's cousin—a fighter for the cause of the Romanian people—who wrote like an angel, the angel with the flaming sword. Father used to contribute to his paper under an assumed name. Mother never knew this. And when father read aloud his own articles, mother always said, "How can anybody see so much misery and injustice in this world? As if there was no God."

"But, Barbara dear, there is misery and injustice in the world," father would answer.

"There is, yes, but not as much as this man says," mother said. "Besides, there *is* a God," she added.

57

"Certainly there is a God, but you heard what Uncle Gherasim said about poverty. He said that it was not God who put poverty on this earth, but man," father said, "and you agreed with him."

"Of course I agreed with him, because I know, everybody knows, that God is good," mother said.

"Well then, misery and injustice is also man's work," father said.

"Certainly it is. Not so much though as that man says. The good Lord would not allow so much. No! Never!" And that was final. In mother's firm belief God had an exact measure for misery and injustice among man.

Patriots like Silvestru Arin had plenty to fight about. The Romanians in Transylvania claimed that this land belonged to them. The Romanian population was larger than the Hungarian; it had been established there since Roman times and was peaceable and industrious. To be ruled by Hungarians was the height of injustice in the eyes of these patriots.

As rulers, the Hungarians considered themselves superior, and the smallest Hungarian functionary treated a Romanian peasant with scorn. If a Romanian peasant asked for a railroad ticket in his own language, which was all he knew, the ticket agent would shout at him in Hungarian that he did not understand the savage tongue. And if the poor man got no help from anyone, he was left in the station, waiting for better luck when the next train came. Sometimes he would have to wait until the following day. He could not sleep in the station waiting room, because if there were no night trains the station master ordered the waiting room locked. And this was but a minor example of the Hungarians' behavior.

58

The Romanian peasant wears a sort of sandal, *opinca,* which in Hungarian is *botchkor.* The Hungarians gave the derogatory name of Botchkorosh—the Sandaled—to the Romanians. Once a Hungarian gendarme sergeant brought in a peasant to the communal house before father and the mayor. The man was accused of some petty theft.

"This Botchkorosh—" the gendarme started to say. Father struck the table with his fist and shouted, "What is the man's name? Tell his name if you are not too stupid, and get out!" The gendarme flushed with anger but he said, "I have done my duty, sir, to arrest him."

"Your duty is to name a prisoner. And what is your name? Do you know it? Or shall I call you Hun, as you call this man Botchkorosh?" father said sternly.

"I am a servant of my government, sir, I know my duty," the gendarme said, aflame with rage.

"Then, servant, I ask your name. You will be reported," father said.

"Mueller Hans is my name, sir," the fellow said. He was frightened now.

"A Saxon," father said to the mayor. Then he took a sheet of paper and wrote a report. He asked the mayor and the orderly to witness it. "You may go," father said to the gendarme.

"The prisoner, sir?" Mueller asked, all mollified now.

"You have no prisoner," father said.

"He, there," Mueller pointed at the peasant.

"What has no name does not exist," father said.

The peasant, who was standing there miserably, watching father, opened his mouth to say something. Father mentioned him to keep silent. The gendarme noticed the man's action. Taking two steps toward him he said in garbled Romanian, "What my name?" He meant to ask the peasant's name, who promptly answered, "Miller Hans."

Baffled, the original Mueller Hans turned to father, then he tramped out of the room. The peasant brightened up at once. "Am I free to go, please, may the Lord bless you?" he said.

"What is your name?" father asked.

"Vasile Tudor."

"You stole!" father said.

"It was not stealing, sir. It was borrowing and returning," the peasant said.

"But you were arrested. Why?"

"Because the man accused me."

"What man?"

"The man I took, that is, I borrowed from."

"What did you borrow? You returned it?"

"It was a lamb. When he came with the gendarme I was about to take the lamb back to him. So he took it himself."

"Where was the lamb?" father asked.

"In the house. Our little boy Michail was playing with it," the peasant said.

"Then you were not about to take it back," father said sharply.

"The thought was in my head, sir," the peasant said, frightened.

"Who is the man?" father asked.

"Ion Arghir, sir. His chickens scratched up my little garden and ate the seeds I planted," the peasant said, complainingly.

Father sent for Arghir. When he came in and saw Vasile he glared at him.

"His chickens, sir, as I said, made a desert of my garden," Vasile hastened to say.

"Liar. Thief," snapped Arghir.

Father shouted at them to be quiet. "We beg your forgiveness, sir," the peasants said in chorus.

Vasile Tudor might have had the "thought in his head" when Arghir and the gendarme arrived at his place, but Arghir told father that they found him sharpening his knife with a whetstone. "And I could see with one eye he meant to slaughter the lamb," Arghir said.

Father had to talk a long time before he could bring about a peaceful settlement between the two. He sentenced Vasile Tudor to give two days' labor to Ion Arghir.

"And the damage to my garden, sir?" Vasile asked.

"Remember, Vasile, the gendarme arrested you. For theft. The law would give you a month in prison. I am giving you twenty-eight days of freedom for the damage you suffered," father said.

"Now I see the light, sir. May the Lord bless you with happy years," Vasile said. They left. The mayor watched them through the window. In the street Vasile said, "I will work for you two days, but not digging your well. No! There I stop."

"Come back then, in there," Arghir said. Vasile glanced at the communal house, and saw the mayor in the window. He raised his hat to the mayor, turned to Arghir and said, "Come, you never understood a joke." He did put in two days at digging Arghir's well.

Father never reported Hans Mueller. He only meant to frighten him. The truth is that he had no grounds for a report against the gendarme, save that he was arrogant toward a peasant, which his superior would not consider an offense. But the threat had an effect on Mueller. When next he came he apologized to father.

These things father took very seriously. Mother said they were small matters. Such things happened everywhere. There are arrogant Romanians too, she said. Besides, the nickname the Hungarians gave the Romanians was not insulting really. The peasants did wear those sandals. The Hungarians and Saxons wore boots. Suppose the Romanians called them "the Booted."

She really said all this to calm father. It did not help. He said the thing went deeper than that. What mother thought small matters reflected the cleavage between the two nations and also the belief of the Hungarians that they were superior to the Romanians because of governing over Transylvania. That should not be, father said. And that is what Silvestru Arin was fighting against.

Every year Arin had to pay fines and once he was imprisoned. Then the worst happened. It was in the dead of winter. We were in bed, Irina and I. We heard voices. Father and a strange man were talking. Mother came to see if we were asleep. She was pale. "Who came, mother?" Irina asked. "A man, dear, now go to sleep," mother said.

In the morning there was no stranger in the house. We had breakfast as usual but when Irina raised her voice telling about her schoolwork, mother hushed her. Father sat silent, lost in thought. It was not the usual morning, with father saying cheerfully, "A new day, children, give your best to it." And when he left, mother saw him to the outside door, where they spoke in low voices.

In the evening Uncle Gherasim came with two men we had not seen before. We did not hear the bells of a sleigh, but one of the men told father it was ready, at Uncle Gherasim's. Mother brought glasses, plum brandy, bread, and black olives. The men took off their sheepskin coats; they were long, down to their ankles. Underneath these they had heavy black woolen coats, nearly as long. These they merely opened. Then I thought they were bandits whom Uncle Gherasim knew and was not afraid of. Each had two pistols in his belt. Irina and I looked at the weapons with big, wondering eyes. Seeing us, Uncle Gherasim said to one of the men, "Are there wolves in the neighborhood?" and he coughed a little.

"There are," one of the men said quietly. His voice was very deep. The other man nodded his head. They had two glasses of brandy each. They drank slowly, munching bread and olives. Then one man said they had better be on their way. Father went out with them. He opened the door of our guest room, which opened on the small hallway. Uncle Gherasim stayed with us. "Shall I tell you a story with wolves?" he asked us. "Yes, Uncle Gherasim, please tell us," Irina said and I echoed the words.

Father came back before Uncle Gherasim had finished the story. His face was red from the cold and his mustaches were white with frost. We did not know he had left the house. Mother looked at him questioningly.

"They are on their way," father said. Mother clasped her hands. Her lips moved a little as when she prayed. Uncle Gherasim finished the story and rose. When he left he said, "Good night, I leave you with the Lord." At the door he said to father, "Those friends of mine have no fear of wolves."

That night Silvestru Arin was taken to a distant village,

near a mountain pass. From there two other men were to guide him over the border into Romania, the following night. It was years later that I learned of this.

The Hungarian government sentenced him *in absentia* —as he had fled before he could be arrested—to three years in prison and seven years' banishment from Transylvania.

For days my parents were not their usual selves. They seemed troubled by something they could not be rid of. Uncle Gherasim alone would cheer them a little. "It is well," he said every evening as soon as he stepped in the house. One time I heard him say, "You can trust those men as you trust your own eyes."

At long last father came home happy again.

"Good news?" mother asked.

"Very good news," father said. He gave a letter to mother. As she read it, her face brightened, and tears came in her eyes. When she finished reading she crossed herself and said, "Thank God." Then she kissed father, Irina, and me. Our home was normal once more.

CHAPTER 8

⊙⊙⊙⊙⊙⊙⊙⊙⊙⊙

MOTHER WEPT EASILY. PERHAPS WEEPING IS NOT the exact description, for actually it was merely that tears came easily into her eyes. This happened when she was sad or very happy.

"You have so many tears, Barbara dear," father said this time, when both of them were so happy with the news.

Mother smiled and said, "Tears cleanse the heart, dear."

It was wonderful how mother could explain things about herself. There was good in sorrow too, according to her. In sorrow you commune with your soul and with God, she said. Her belief was that the saints sorrowed for us mortals because we were sinful. And the Savior had the greatest of all sorrows because he understood man with holy understanding. That is, perfectly. She got this belief from the images on the icons, where the saints and the Savior were depicted with the saddest expressions imaginable. Who has ever seen a cheerful saint? They are all pale, emaciated, with large, sad eyes in haggard faces. They are awkward, too, in their movements, as if indeed

65

the body were a burden that they would shake off the shoulders of their soul.

But we had one icon made by Osip Orloff, the Russian icon maker who lived in our village, a giant of a man. This icon represented Saint Peter standing at the gates of heaven with a key as large as a mallet in his hand. A weapon really, in the hands of this wide-shouldered saint. And his eyes were as watchful as they were sad, but one felt that his sadness sprang from the monotony of his function, not from sorrowing over the troubles of men. This Saint Peter was the only saint that had a body worth its keep. Osip did not have the heart to give such an important watcher a body so frail as other saints had.

And in a way, Saint Peter is not as important as he appears, for if the other saints intervene in favor of a man's soul, he simply has to open the gates and let it into Paradise.

.Father bought this icon because he liked Osip and believed that he did justice to the saint. Of course, this icon stood alone, on a piece of the wall between two windows of our large room, while the other saints were ranged on the opposite wall. They looked at Saint Peter with the same sorrowful compassion as they looked upon us mortals.

Saint Peter's day falls at wheat harvest and it is celebrated by the peasants with new bread baked from the first wheat of the year. In our family we had a double celebration since I am named after this saint. Mother would have preferred to have a more saintly Saint Peter on the icon than the one Osip depicted. This one was entirely too earthly, just a muzhik with a halo around his big head.

66

Father said, "Barbara dear, you want our son to be sturdy. It is only proper that his saint should be a model for him."

"Yes, dear, I do want our son to be sturdy. That is our concern. But a saint should be a model for the soul," mother said.

"Osip can't depict a soul, my dear. He has never seen one," father said.

"He has never seen Saint Peter either," mother said.

"No, he has not, but he knows that all saints had bodies. And fishermen are no weaklings," father said.

Mother said it was natural enough for fishermen to be robust as long as they plied their trade, but when they fished for souls, grossness of body was unbecoming, to say the least. She might say it was gaudy arrogance. Mother loved to qualify adjectives, which amused father. He would say sometimes that the soup mother cooked had the tastiest taste and the meat was the tenderest tender.

Once I was eating a pear mother gave me and said it was the goodest good pear. Mother looked at me earnestly and said, "My little soul, it is a sin to mimic anybody, even your father."

I believed father was the greatest of all men. Whatever he did was right even if it seemed wrong to others. I told mother what I believed. She said of course father was a wonderful man, but I must never forget that I had a mother, too. "Everybody has two parents, my little soul," she said. Because I did not understand what she meant I wondered why she told me such an obvious thing as if it really was important.

Our parents were strict with us, but not in the same

67

manner. Mother was firm in a gentle way, and patient. Father was curt. Mother guided us. Father commanded. We never dared ask him the why of one of his orders. It was issued; it must be obeyed. If in obeying I felt miserable, mother would explain to me the reason of father's command. I loved her with all my heart, and was happy when people said I resembled her. But when they said that my sister resembled father I resented it. She was not at all wonderful and she pouted when angry, while father never did. After a fine explosion, his anger soon was dissipated.

When I complained to Uncle Gherasim about Irina and said she did not resemble father, he said she did, but the feminine nature was added too and I would understand that when I grew up. I believed Uncle Gherasim, for next to father he was the most wonderful man. But since everybody reminded me that I could not understand this or that before I grew up, which annoyed me, I wished Uncle Gherasim had not said it too.

"Why can't I understand everything I am told, Uncle Gherasim?"

"You do, Peter, but your world is smaller, so your understanding is smaller, too," Uncle Gherasim said.

"Is your world bigger than mine, Uncle Gherasim?" I asked.

"It is, Peter, with so many years bigger," Uncle Gherasim said.

"Do years make the world grow?" I asked.

"Yes, Peter. The years make the world grow," Uncle Gherasim said.

"How many years can the world grow?" I asked.

"As many years as people live," Uncle Gherasim said.

"How big will the world grow, Uncle Gherasim?" I asked.

"So big until it reaches to God," Uncle Gherasim said.

◊◊◊◊◊◊◊◊◊◊

CHAPTER 9

THE SUMMER AFTER AUNT VERONICA DIED, UNCLE Gherasim took me to the mountains. Mother was concerned, for I had never been away from home alone and to be in that wilderness—as she said—might frighten me. "He is not seven yet, Uncle Gherasim," she said.

"Now is the age to lay the foundation. A human being is like a building. If the foundation is good the building will stand," Uncle Gherasim said.

"And what will he eat?" mother asked. "He is not spoiled, of course, but he is used to our food." The truth is that while I preferred, say, boiled beef to salt fish, I could eat every kind of food. My appetite never failed me.

"He will have the kidney fat of the land," Uncle Gherasim said to mother. "He will be a little man when we come back."

Uncle Gherasim came for me at dawn with his two horses, both saddled, and the saddles padded with sheepskins. My parents came out into the yard, mother holding me by the hand.

"How will he travel?" she asked Uncle Gherasim.

"Like a Haiduk, in the saddle," Uncle Gherasim said. He took my hand. Mother embraced me. Her eyes were full of tears. Uncle Gherasim lifted me into the saddle.

"He will ride alone?" mother asked, frightened.

"He is as safe as sitting in a chair," Uncle Gherasim said.

"Hold onto the pommel, Peter," father said. "You are not afraid, I know." He patted my hands. Mother was weeping.

Uncle Gherasim mounted the other horse. My horse was tied to his. "We leave you with the Lord," he said, indicating we were ready.

Mother walked out into the street, holding onto my leg. "God be with you, my dear little soul. Take good care of him, Uncle Gherasim," she said and kissed my bare knee. Father slapped me on the back, as he did to his friend Ciobanel when he left us, and said, "You are a Haiduk now, Peter, happy journey."

I felt very brave riding on horseback and fancied I was really a Haiduk, although my horse was tied to Uncle Gherasim's. Therefore I allowed he was my captain and felt no shame riding behind him.

Every now and again Uncle Gherasim would turn his head and ask if I was all right. Certainly I was. He had put the wide wooden stirrups way high for my feet. Once I took one hand off the pommel, then for a short distance let go of it entirely. I was teaching myself to ride a horse, I imagined, and felt very proud.

When Uncle Gherasim looked back later I said, "I can ride with my hands free, Uncle Gherasim."

"Of course you can, Peter, but since you have nothing else to do with your hands, keep them on the pommel," he said. I loved Uncle Gherasim because he treated me as if I were a grown person.

When the sun was midway to noon, Uncle Gherasim found a shady place at the foot of the hill that rose right from the margin of the road, and we stopped there. He helped me dismount and we watered the horses at the river. I held the end of the one halter and, after the horse drank, led him back to our place.

"You can manage a horse well, Peter," Uncle Gherasim said. I believed him, although my horse, having had enough water, simply turned from the river and all I had to do was hasten to walk ahead of him, holding onto the end of the halter.

While we were eating the bread and cheese Uncle Gherasim brought along—he would not open my bag of provisions, saying we should have that for supper—the head of the flood waters from the dam up the river came roaring down, carrying the pine logs toward the paper mill. There was a great noise of rushing water, logs clattering as they were hurled together and thrown against the rocks on the river bank. When the logs were jammed against the bank some were forced upright and carried along in the crushing grip of the other logs. Others were thrown clear and left on the bank, with the sun shimmering on their wet surfaces.

It was wonderful to watch them. They seemed alive and playful in the water and I felt sorry for the ones left behind. Uncle Gherasim told me everything about these logs. They were cut in the great forest, cleaned of bark, and "given to the river to carry them to the paper mill," he said. "But the river is not strong enough to carry such a burden. So they built a dam right above the place where

72

the logs are cut. All night long the water gathers in the dam. In the morning the flood gates are opened and the river gets help to carry the logs." He told me that the paper mill was very far and it took several days for the first logs to reach there. After that there would be others arriving each day. In the autumn, before winter sets in and the river freezes, the men would come down and throw the logs on the banks into the river so none would be left behind.

By noon we left the river road and took a horse trail. We were getting into hilly country. At the top of a hill we rested the horses and I looked at the range of other hills. They all had names. Uncle Gherasim told them to me.

We took a long time with our midday meal so the horses could feed on the grass bordering a birch copse. But then I became drowsy and Uncle Gherasim told me to sleep a little on the blanket he spread out between the trees.

We stopped in the evening with Uncle Gherasim's friend, Pavel Boncea. The house nestled against the side of a hill in a shallow declivity that looked like the lap of a seated woman. Boncea's wife set the table and they invited us to eat with them. Uncle Gherasim thanked them but said we must eat the roasted chicken mother had put up for us. "We have it and we must eat it," he said. I fell asleep at the table and woke up in the morning in a nest of fresh hay on the barn floor.

Good Uncle Gherasim. He not only had put me to bed there, but had undressed me and put my nightshirt on me. Mother had asked him to have me sleep in it.

That day I saw, here and there, clusters of houses and plum orchards. Sometimes I saw just one hut, very for-

73

lorn looking. Uncle Gherasim knew the names of all the hamlets and villages and even the names of people who lived in the lone houses.

"We shall be where we are going before the sun sets, Peter," he told me. I was so tired now that when he took me off the horse at noon I could not stand on my feet. Uncle Gherasim did not laugh at my staggering. He took my hand and held my shoulder too and said, "We will walk a little to limber up, both of us."

When we reached the mountain plateau, the sun was at the horizon, but far back in the lower hilly country the night was falling. The whole stretch was in deep blue shadow. Uncle Gherasim said, "Night comes earlier to those in the low land."

Thousands of sheep were slowly moving across the high tableland, sunlight on their backs. They looked like jammed ice floes on a slow-flowing river. In the distance were two huts and the pen for the sheep. We got there before the sheep. An old man met us. His face was the color of copper, very wrinkled, but his eyes were clear. "Welcome with the Lord," he greeted us. "May your health be good, Achim," Uncle Gherasim answered.

"We expected you. Tudor brought word you were coming," Achim said. He came to help me dismount.

"And who might you be, little gentleman?" he asked. He called me so because I was not dressed in peasant clothes. I told him my name. "I know now," he said, "may you grow up and may your parents live."

The hut was larger than it looked from the outside. There was a big hearth at one end. A good fire burned under a large round-bottomed caldron that stood on an iron tripod. Along two walls were narrow board beds

74

resting on heavy wooden legs made of round pieces of timber. All the beds had heavy frieze blankets on them for cover. The place smelled of wood smoke, virgin wool, and cheese. And from the hearth came the delicious odor of lamb meat and onions.

Uncle Gherasim sniffed and said, "And we came with the hunger of the wolf, Achim."

"It is good. Oana is cooking a stew. It must be ready," Achim said. Shortly, Oana came with two large buckets of spring water. She was a young woman with very red cheeks and black eyes. She greeted us.

"You have hungry people here, Oana," Achim said.

"Presently the table will be spread," Oana said. Her cheeks became redder still. She hurried about.

We were at the table when the three shepherds arrived. They greeted us, crossed themselves, and sat down at the table. This was my first experience eating with a wooden fork, but I managed well enough. The lamb stew was very good. Oana gave me choice pieces of the lean meat, for Uncle Gherasim had told her I did not like the fat. She sat by me on the shorter bench at the end of the table. Every now and again she leaned her head close to my face and asked, "Do you like it, Peter?" My answer was yes, to which she said, "Eat then, for your good health."

After supper the shepherds played music, all three of them together. One of them, Tudor, a tall, lean, hirsute man and somber when he did not smile, had the largest fife. Nicolai, a young lad of sixteen, had the smallest. Nicolai played the melody, the other two the obbligato. It was beautiful. Then Uncle Gherasim asked Achim to play. His fife was as large as Tudor's but it was ornate with

75

fine lines cut in the wood in a very intricate pattern, and the wood was brown with age.

"What shall I play?" Achim asked.

"What your heart asks for," Uncle Gherasim answered.

Achim played a sad tune in a low key. Oana became pensive. She put her arm around me, held me close to her, and we rocked to the slow cadence of the melody. Then suddenly Achim started a brisk dance tune. Tudor jumped up, danced, and the other two shepherds joined in, Uncle Gherasim and Oana clapping their hands. Her mood changed instantly. She picked me up and made me dance with her. I jumped up and down and let her twirl me around, which soon made me dizzy. "No more, please, Oana," I said and she swung me up in her arms and placed me on the bench.

It was at this point that I thought of home, watching the dancers as I had watched them at the wedding of Uncle Stefan and Alexandra. For a moment I wished father, mother, and Irina were here, and then I fell asleep.

I woke up in the morning, my face cool and moist with dew. I was in the open, on a bed of sheepskins, wrapped in a frieze blanket. Nearby was Uncle Gherasim's empty "nest."

The sheep already were grazing a short distance away. Smoke came through the chimney of the hut. As I struggled out of the blanket Uncle Gherasim appeared from behind the hut. He helped me, then he said, "Now for your morning bath, Peter."

The grass chilled my feet as Uncle Gherasim led me to the spring. "The dew is good," he said. The spring was enclosed with a fence to keep the sheep out. They drank from the overflow that ran out in a long wooden trough.

In this enclosure the grass was high and heavy with dew.

"Now," Uncle Gherasim said, "take your nightgown off. Here is where you bathe, Peter."

"In the spring?" I asked.

"No, in the grass," he said. "Just stretch out, Peter, and roll in it before the warmth of your body leaves you."

I threw myself in the dew-drenched grass. It was very cold. "Keep rolling, Peter. Don't lift your head."

After the first shock it felt good to roll in the soft, fragrant grass, and I thought of the mountain sprites Uncle Gherasim had told us about. They were beautiful because they bathed in dew, and the peasants say, "Look at the lovely girl, she must bathe in dew."

After the bath, Uncle Gherasim made me run around the enclosure until I was out of breath and warm. When I first awoke the sun had been on the high mountain peak and now it spilled over the plateau, a flood of light which seemed to bathe the grazing sheep. As we walked into the hut, Uncle Gherasim's long shadow disappeared suddenly at the door.

We had breakfast of fresh corn mush and the rich milk of ewes. The three shepherds were gone, so it was Uncle Gherasim, Oana, Achim, and I who sat at table. I felt very strong and wondered if I had already grown much during the night and the short time of the morning.

Mother's last words to me when I left were, "Be happy, my little soul." I was very happy. And in my happiness I thought of home, but did not long to be there. Rather, I wished my parents and Irina were with me in the mountains. But then I thought too that if they were with me I would be less free, because both father and mother would say what I should do and Irina would sometimes annoy

77

me. Once or twice I wondered if it were a sin for me to prefer the freedom I had. For, being with Uncle Gherasim, I felt no restriction of any kind and what he made me do was always very pleasant. He told me about sheep and the making of cheese, and showed me the kind of fir trees that produced a gum that was pleasant to chew.

This gum is fragrant, almost white, and after much chewing it becomes pink and brittle, at which stage it must be discarded.

Uncle Gherasim also allowed me to use the knife he had given me, to whittle a piece of soft green wood, but this I was allowed to do only in his presence.

Oana pampered me a little, feeding me between meals with sweet cheese—that is, until Uncle Gherasim caught her at it.

"He is not to be stuffed, Oana. Peter is used to regular meals at regular hours. I have charge of him. This boy is a race horse, not a drudge animal," he said.

I liked the sweet cheese, but then, I was proud to be a race horse. I ran and jumped and acted the part of a spirited horse such as Uncle Gherasim had in his stories. My regret was that I had not at least two wings like the eagle we saw one morning, if not four like the wonder horses in fairy tales.

Uncle Gherasim had decided "to put strength" in my body, he said. Mountain air would clear my blood and my lungs too, he said, and would give me the eyesight of eagles. He made me breathe deeply, counting to five while I inhaled. "Now," he said, "let the air out of you slowly, while I count to fifteen."

Three times daily he gave me this exercise for about three minutes each. At first it made me a little dizzy and

78

I let the air out of me before the count of fifteen. But later I managed to Uncle Gherasim's satisfaction and without getting dizzy.

"We are on the good road now," he said, "and we have reached the next stage." This next stage was bathing in whey. There was a large vat in which the milk was gathered and made to curdle with contents from the stomach of a suckling lamb. When the milk was properly set, the curds were taken out in cloth bags and pressed under heavy boards weighted down with large stones. The liquid that remained in the vat was the whey. This Uncle Gherasim warmed in a large caldron, poured into the wooden trough, and my bath was ready.

Each time I took this bath I smelled like a lump of cottage cheese until the following morning when my bathing in dew washed the odor away. It had to be so, because Uncle Gherasim said the beneficial virtue of the whey must not be washed off with water for twenty-four hours.

The result of Uncle Gherasim's treatment was wonderful. In two weeks I got to feel marvelously well, although I had been healthy enough before. And my sun tan was as deep as a gypsy's. With a large sheepskin cap on my head, Uncle Gherasim made me lie in the sun. We started with ten or fifteen minutes until I acquired a good tan, when he let me stay a whole hour under the blazing sun. I put on sandals only after the sun set. Wearing these, I felt as if I had wings on my feet. I raced with one of the dogs, a good-natured, shaggy animal that not only won the race but invariably knocked me down once to the goal and once back. Then he would stand over me as if laughing, and to make me feel good, would proceed to lick my face.

79

If I did not get to my feet soon enough the dog would take hold of my vest at the shoulder and try to lift me.

One evening Achim played and Oana and the shepherds danced, but Achim got tired of playing before the dancers got tired of dancing. When they asked him to play more he said, "I would had I the fife that Pacala got from the Lord."

"Burn a bag of incense in the name of God, Achim, as Pacala did and maybe you will get such a fife from the Lord," Uncle Gherasim said.

"Yes, but I am not sixteen years old as Pacala was when God gave him the magic fife. I carry seventy years on my back and a load of sins too. I would need many bags of incense to win such favor from the Lord. And, maybe if I were carried up to heaven by an angel, as Pacala was carried, I would ask another gift from the Lord, not a fife," Achim said.

"What would you ask?" Oana put the question.

"Well, lass," Achim said, looking at Oana with smiling eyes, "I would ask the Lord to take fifty years off my shoulders and let me stay like that on this good earth until I ask Him myself for old age and then for eternal rest."

"Then you would stay young forever because you would never ask for old age," one of the young shepherds said.

"Who knows, lad. Man is so made that in time he gets tired of the sweetest things. But what I know now is that old age came long before I got tired of being young," Achim said.

By this time my eyes were heavy with sleep. I heard Oana say, "The little one is gone into the world of dreams." More I did not hear. In the morning Oana told me it was she who had put me to bed "under the stars."

80

CHAPTER 10

๑๑๑๑๑๑๑๑๑๑๑๑๑

A FEW DAYS LATER A MAN CAME WHO TOLD US A story worthy of Pacala. He was a short fellow, very fat, and rode a donkey. Uncle Gherasim knew him well. He called him by his nickname, Berbec, which is ram in Romanian. The fellow had something about him that made one think of a ram. His hair was thick and curly; he had a low forehead and his full beard was curly too, and grown high on his cheeks so his small eyes seemed encircled with wool. A great mimic he was, too. When he dismounted he opened a big mouth and started to bray and kept it up until his donkey answered him.

"And what brings you this way, Berbec, we have not seen you these past two summers," Uncle Gherasim said.

"Well, Gherasim, I am looking for yesterday. Every tomorrow is catching up with me," Berbec said, making a sad face. "You see, Gherasim, life has a trick of running like the days, in one direction only, so I decided to go against the stream."

"How are Lisaveta and the children?" Uncle Gherasim asked.

"She is well, Gherasim, carrying our fifth—maybe a son —and the children bounce about like fledglings fallen from a nest," Berbec said. "They are always hungry and as for me, I am perishing right now. Just look." He pulled in his belly and his belt dropped to his groins.

"There will be corn mush and sour milk, Berbec," Uncle Gherasim said.

"That is good food, Gherasim, but my nose tells me there is stew hereabouts. Good fat stew that makes the corn mush go down without rubbing gullet," Berbec said. He looked even sadder now. He let the donkey nibble the grass at the rear of the hut and lowered himself down on his haunches, chewing the end of a straw.

Oana came out from the hut. Berbec raised his head slowly and greeted her in a thin voice. "May your seed be blessed, woman," and he made the sign of the cross over her as priests do in blessing.

Oana blushed, lowered her head and said, "Welcome, pilgrim." She mistook Berbec for a traveling monk.

"Pilgrim I am, good woman, and lost I am on the narrow and crooked road of this life," Berbec answered in a high-pitched falsetto.

Oana clasped her hands in pity and went back in the hut. A few moments later she came out with a large piece of cold corn bread and a bowl of sour milk. "Partake of this, pilgrim, in the name of the Lord," Oana said.

"The name of the Lord be blessed. Amen," Berbec said taking the food.

Uncle Gherasim turned away, pretending to look for something, and laughed quietly. When Oana went back in the hut he said to Berbec, "Eat with good appetite, pilgrim."

82

"Thank you, good Christian, this will hold me until the stew is ready," Berbec droned in his natural voice, only he made it nasal with his nose all screwed up.

We sat on the ground, Uncle Gherasim, Berbec, and I, this being my afternoon hour of rest. I should have taken my nap but asked Uncle Gherasim to let me sit there, for I was fascinated by this visitor.

Having finished eating, Berbec took out his pipe and a pouch made of pig's bladder. Very deliberately he stuffed his pipe, then he produced a leaf-shaped piece of steel, flint, and punk. He struck the flint with the steel, ignited the punk, blew on it, and placed it in the pipe. He performed all this with eyes half closed as if he were in deep meditation. But soon as he had the pipe thoroughly lighted he opened his eyes and smiled broadly. "Gherasim," he said, "there are people who say it was the devil who gave men the tobacco and taught them to smoke. If it was the devil, he is my friend. But the tax collector, Gherasim, whoever invented him is my mortal enemy. May he roast in the depths of hell unto eternity."

"The tax collector is only a servant of the government. It is the government that needs the money," Uncle Gherasim said.

"The government you say. I never saw the government. Where is the government? What is it, man, woman, beast, or fowl?" Berbec asked.

"You do not see the government, Berbec, you see its work," Uncle Gherasim said.

"Then the government is the devil, the unholy black one, whose work you see but never see him," Berbec said. "And why does the government need all that money, Gherasim? It takes from me, the bread from my children,

I can say, and it takes from you. Well, but you have enough for the devil too, but I, a poor man, with a child coming every fourteen months to the day—where is the justice, Gherasim, I ask you?"

"For one thing, Berbec, we have an army. The common soldier serves three years. He is fed and clothed, is given equipment, is housed, and he does not earn his bread," Uncle Gherasim said.

"There!" Berbec said, "the first trick of the devil. Take thousands of young men from their work and make drones of them for you and me to feed. It is unholy, Gherasim. A great sin too, for did not God tell us to earn our bread by the sweat of our brow?"

"We do earn our bread just so, Berbec, and feeding the soldiers we sweat more," Uncle Gherasim said.

"That is where the devil comes in, Gherasim. Why should I sweat for others? And why do we need all this army? To give the officers men to drill and keep them in fat?" Berbec asked.

"The army is a protection against the enemy, Berbec. The army is like you are to your home and family, a protector," Uncle Gherasim said.

"Look Gherasim, first of all I took a wife. We have children. That is as God wills it. Multiply, He tells us. Well and good. I do my share as a good God-fearing Christian. Now, the wife is mine, the children are mine, and I belong to them body and soul. But an army, Gherasim! What relation is it to me? And what am I to it?" Berbec asked.

"Let us put it this way, Berbec. The country is your mother, the government is your father. Now then, is not the duty of the father to protect both of you, your mother

84

and yourself? It is. And the army is the weapon," Uncle Gherasim said.

"That sounds good, Gherasim. The country is my mother. Beautiful. I love my mother. With all my heart I love her. But my father—the government, as you say— no. I do not love him or it. Not at all. And the weapon, I have no use for it," Berbec said.

"And in case the enemy comes, warring on you? It comes to ravish your country. What will you do then, Berbec?" Uncle Gherasim said.

"What enemy, Gherasim? And how will he come?"

"Any enemy. And he will come with an army."

"He will come because he has an army, then."

"Yes! Without an army he could not come."

"Then, because we have an army, some people will think we are their enemy," Berbec said.

"Countries have armies for the purpose of defense," Uncle Gherasim said.

"So all have armies, and everybody is everybody's enemy, because nobody knows which will jump on which," Berbec said.

I became very drowsy and Uncle Gherasim told me to lie down on the blanket. Instantly I was asleep. When I woke the sheep were coming, following Tudor, the other two shepherds and the dogs following the flock. Uncle Gherasim and Berbec were in the milk cellar where I heard them talking. There was a saddle horse tied to one of the fence posts. A big, black horse, stamping its feet and lashing with its tail. From the cellar came now and again a deep, booming voice and laughter.

I walked over to the cellar. There was Popa Radu, sitting on an upturned tub.

"The little man is up," he said, seeing me at the door. "Come here, son," he said. He held out his huge hand for me to kiss. "So, they are bathing you in whey. You smell like a milk tub, son," he said, looking me up and down. "I saw your parents. Everybody is well at home," he told me and pulled my ear. Then he turned to Uncle Gherasim and said, "You have made a gypsy of the little fellow; his mother won't know him."

"I am making a man of him, your reverence," Uncle Gherasim said.

"Does he rub you down with bear grease, too?" Popa Radu asked me and laughed.

"He is past the age of bear grease," Uncle Gherasim said.

"Well, I hear the sheep coming, Gherasim. Have my five hundred head increased?" he asked paying no more attention to me.

"They might have, your reverence, had there been five hundred to begin with," Uncle Gherasim said.

"How many were there then? They are eating my sheep," Popa Radu said.

"Four hundred and twenty ewes, sixty lambs—mixed —and two rams. We have counted them together," Uncle Gherasim said.

Popa Radu started to laugh. His whole big body shook. And then he said, "I trust you, Gherasim, but I believe in miracles. Are we going to eat soon? And not one of my lambs."

"No, your reverence, I did not know you were coming. It is one of my scrawny lambs, just hide and bones, that Tudor slaughtered this morning. It is a pity we did not know you were coming, for there is a brown lamb in your flock, fat as a melon with fine curly wool that would make a beautiful pelt for a cap," Uncle Gherasim said.

"You thief. I remember that one brown lamb. A poor creature. It was yours, not mine," Popa Radu said.

"It is no longer poor. Well, it is mine then, and maybe the one stewing now Tudor took from your flock," Uncle Gherasim said. "By mistake, certainly," he added.

"Then I will eat the stew alone," Popa Radu said.

"Woe is me," chanted Berbec from his corner. "I am a poor pilgrim, your reverence."

"You are a fat sinner. Three days fasting would do your soul good," Popa Radu said.

"My poor soul could not profit from the torment of my body, your reverence," Berbec said.

"I am a priest, my duty on earth is to help souls along the right path," Popa Radu said.

Berbec had heard of this giant of a priest who boomed his sermons so the sinners quaked and swung the censer with the glowing coals so vigorously that the kneeling people had to bend their heads low out of its way. He was afraid Popa Radu might deprive him of the stew.

Father used to say that Popa Radu would force his way into heaven, Saint Peter or no Saint Peter. But mother said that he had a big and good heart, for it was God who gave him that great body and boisterous nature. It was no sin, she said, to have such heartiness and such abundance of life. She admired his enormous appetite too. When he came to us mother put a whole chicken before him, boiled or roasted, and Popa Radu ate it all, chewing the ends of the larger bones and sucking out the marrow without belching once after he did away with a plateful of pancakes for dessert. He also drank a full bottle of wine and all that happened to him was that he had to open his belt a few notches and what was visible of his face—he had so much beard on it—became a little redder.

"I can do penance much better with a full belly, your reverence," Berbec said pleadingly.

"That is what you say. I do not know it. So we shall try you first with fasting," Popa Radu said.

"Woe is me," moaned Berbec, "I shall give up my ghost prematurely."

"If that happens I shall see it goes to the right place," Popa Radu said.

"Forgive me, reverend father, but there is no more right place for it than where it is now," Berbec said.

"You cannot know that, my son," Popa Radu said unctuously.

At this point their dialogue was interrupted by Oana. She announced that dinner was ready. We followed Popa Radu into the hut. Berbec was the last to enter.

Popa Radu took the place of honor, at the head of the table. And Berbec was not left out; he was given a corner of the table and the end of the bench on which the three shepherds sat. But the condition set by Uncle Gherasim was that Berbec tell a story, a true story, not one drawn from his fancy.

Popa Radu said he would see to it that Berbec be excommunicated if he inserted the smallest untruth in the story.

"I will comb it with the tight comb of my judgment before I tell it," Berbec said.

"You should be using one on your beard, which you keep scratching," Popa Radu said.

"The itch is a natural one, your reverence, to satisfy my fingers, which can't be idle," Berbec said.

"Tell the story then, Berbec," Uncle Gherasim said.

Berbec swallowed his last mouthful, wiped his mouth with the back of his hand, and began.

"My place is on the side of a mountain, a flat ledge on which the soil is rich because the rains have washed down on it good earth and spread it there as we spread food on the table at a wedding or a funeral feast. On the hills below are beech woods and in the valley are corn fields of the villages scattered there.

"On this ledge my little house stands. I have a small garden and an orchard with, say, fifty fruit trees—mostly plum, a few apple, and six pear trees.

"Right in the center of the orchard I have a pergamuth pear tree. The fruit of this tree is beautiful; gold, with a breath of pink, just a small spot of it like the flush on a baby's cheek. But for the taste of this pear I have no words. A fig would blush if I compared it with such a pear. And the flavor—well, with the leave of his reverence—is like myrrh.

"Now, these pears are in season about the time the corn is half ripe. I let the fruit ripen on the tree and every morning gather what drop during the night. I have always done so since the tree started to give fruit and that is ten or twelve years now. Then last year, I went out to gather the pears one morning and there was not one on the ground. The next morning the same, the third morning just so too.

" 'This is unholy,' I said to my wife. 'Tonight I shall watch! It was full moon. I loaded the gun with heavy lead and a goodly charge of powder and climbed up in the tree, where I made a seat with boards and screened it with hazel branches and straw. The ripe pears kept dropping. I heard them fall.

"It must have been midnight for I heard the cock crow when there was a noise from the side of the precipice. It came nearer, then I heard a grunt. It was a wild boar strolling toward the tree. So you are the thief, I said to myself, when suddenly something like a bundle of straw came rolling down the mountain side at the corner of the orchard. A bear! The creature moved its head slowly to left and to right as it walked, without making a noise, toward the pear tree. Now I was puzzled and frightened too. This beast might smell me in the tree and I am lost. I made ready with the gun and watched the boar raise its head; it grunted and then went on snatching up the fruit from the ground. It was a big animal with long tusks. The bear was near the boar and he, too, started eating the pears. Which one shall I shoot, I asked myself? The boar we can eat and I can sell the bristles and tan the hide and make sandals for my whole family from it. We can eat the bear too, if it is not too old, and its pelt would bring a good price, I reckoned. But something, I don't know what, decided me to shoot the boar. The two creatures were close, one to the other. I aim at the boar, aim between its shoulders and fire. The wild creature grunts, strikes at the bear sideways with its large head and gores him, then it leaps forward and falls. The bear growls, paws several times, tries to rear up and crashes on its side. He paws the ground, tries to rise. His belly is ripped open. His entrails are coming out like wet rags from an overturned wash tub. The boar is still as a piece of timber. I am all sweaty from excitement. A miracle, I mumble and cross myself three times. I am a good believer, your reverence, so I know the Lord helped me. Here, with one shot, He gave me two preys. Slowly I get down from my hiding place. The bear is not dead. It paws feebly but can't move otherwise. I go over and drag the boar to the house and take the ax to finish the agony of the bear. But when I get back, the creature is dead.

"So, your reverence and good people, the Lord gave me and my family food for the whole winter and footwear too, besides a good bearskin which keeps my four children warm in bed on the coldest nights. This is the story and is the truth from beginning to end, all in one piece and the same throughout like this slice of corn bread on the table," Berbec concluded.

"What did you do with the bear meat?" Popa Radu asked.

"I cut up the carcass and hung the pieces in the attic to get smoked. We ate a good deal of the meat fresh. It was a little tough, but sweet and good to taste," Berbec said.

"Shall we believe his story, Gherasim? You know this sinner better than I," Popa Radu said.

"It is true, holiness, I saw the boar's head and the bear's hide, else I would certainly believe we have a new Pacala with us," Uncle Gherasim said.

"So then, I have to trust you, although this sinner might have got the boar's head from some hunter and the bear's hide from a gypsy whose creature died of old age," Popa Radu said.

"It is the truth, naked or sacred, as your holiness might choose," Berbec said.

Then the shepherds teased him. One said the bear

would not be so chummy with a wild boar; the other said the wild creatures would have smelled him and not come near the tree.

"As to the first, I will say that thieves don't look for fleas in each other's hair, and to the second, it is enough to tell that wild creatures smell what they are after, not what is in ambush," Berbec said. He had a ready answer for whatever they said.

Uncle Gherasim took me out and put me to bed. Two dogs slept close by on the ground. I fell asleep to the sound of singing. The booming voice I knew was Popa Radu's, and the high-pitched voice was Oana's. When I woke in the morning, the sheep were already grazing and Popa Radu was with Uncle Gherasim coming from the spring. Popa Radu's beard and mustaches were wet, his face very red. Berbec had gone, Uncle Gherasim told me, with a large piece of cheese from him and a curt blessing from Popa Radu.

During breakfast Popa Radu complained that his sheep did not look so well as Uncle Gherasim's. That was not as should be. In the village nobody had oxen, cows, or goats like the shepherd of the Lord. He could not understand why his sheep should be inferior even to Uncle Gherasim's, although he was known in the whole district for his cleverness at sheep raising.

"I gave much time and care to get this breed," Uncle Gherasim said.

"So have I and I got two of your best rams—you told me they were—and still my sheep look poorer than yours," Popa Radu said.

"Yes, your reverence, but I selected the ewes too, year after year," Uncle Gherasim said.

92

Popa Radu smoothed his beard and frowned. Then Uncle Gherasim said, "And maybe the cross we painted on the sheep protected them from the evil eye," he chuckled.

Popa Radu smote the table with his fist. "So, you old sinner, you took the holy sign to serve your purpose," he boomed. Then he roared with laughter. "I will teach you a lesson. Today they will paint a cross on all my sheep," he said. His sheep were marked with a blue circle on their backs, while Uncle Gherasim's had a large red cross.

The three shepherds spent a good part of the day painting crosses on Popa Radu's sheep. But this cross was smaller than those on Uncle Gherasim's flock, for it had to be painted in the circle already there.

⊙⊙⊙⊙⊙⊙⊙⊙⊙⊙⊙⊙

CHAPTER 11

IN THE EARLY MORNING OF THE FOLLOWING DAY POPA Radu left. His saddle bags were loaded with sweet and seasoned cheese. Before mounting his horse he pulled my ear, slapped my face, and said he would see my parents and tell them Uncle Gherasim was torturing me with his unholy baths. I was ready to cry but Uncle Gherasim assured me that the giant priest had a heart of gold as big as the church bell, and was only teasing me.

Under Uncle Gherasim's care I was getting stronger every day. Then too, twice a day Oana managed to give me between meals a large piece of sweet cheese, a secret we both kept from Uncle Gherasim, neither of us feeling too guilty about it.

"If you are hungry, Peter, it is natural you should eat. We must not forget that you are growing," Oana said.

I was very fond of her because she did not treat me as a little boy except for telling me I was growing. And she was so healthy and cheerful. She sang when she worked and each time she met me she bent down, pressed me to her, and kissed me on the cheeks.

94

One time when Tudor, the oldest shepherd—he was twenty-five-years old—saw her embrace me he said, "May it quench the fire in your heart, Oana."

"Longing for berries one eats the leaves," she said, and laughed. Tudor took off his cap and hurled it against the wall of the hut. Oana picked up the cap and started to put it on her head, then threw it to him and ran into the hut.

"It is the hungry eyes of these young men that make a blooming rose of your cheeks," Achim said to Oana at supper.

"No," she answered, "it is my good blood."

"She is burying her youth in the grave of old age," Tudor said. The younger shepherds laughed.

"The years are good to me, they run over me like water over brook stones," Oana said, laughing.

"And one day old age will slap you in the face," Achim said.

"Not if I see it coming," Oana answered.

"But you will not see or hear it. It comes on tiptoes, wrapped in deception," Achim said.

"I can't be afraid of what I do not see or hear," Oana said.

"Then I shall climb silently to the attic in the dead darkness of night," Tudor said.

"You know I pull up the ladder when I go up," Oana said.

"Some night you will forget," Tudor said.

"Yes, yes! Time comes for everything," Achim said. "One day you will lose a tooth. The first to go. Like the first dry branch on a tree. And you know it is lost forever."

95

"You can't make me sad," Oana said. She laughed. Her teeth were sound and white, and the gums red.

That evening there was no dancing nor singing. They were in a mood for talking. They asked Achim to tell a story—"so we can rest our tongues," Tudor said.

"A story you want. Life is a story. Everybody's life is a story. Told once, and time swallows it, piecemeal. We eat food, time eats us," Achim said.

"You remember what you lived through, Achim, time left you that," Uncle Gherasim said. He had been silent until then.

"Yes, time left me that, but that's like the echo from a cave, or the afterglow when the sun has vanished from sight," Achim said.

"You can live through what you remember," Tudor said.

"No, Tudor, you cannot. I am close to seventy. Can I live through what I remember from the time I was twenty? No! I cannot," Achim said. "The afterglow will give you some light, but warmth—no. The sun is gone. The time when I was twenty is gone too. There is no warmth in remembrance."

"Don't you ever think back?" Tudor asked.

"Not by choice. Something might come and throw my thoughts back into the past, suddenly," Achim said.

"Having memory is to live twice as long as your days," Tudor said. "I have thought much about it."

"Well, you might think so, Tudor. You are the kind who looks inside himself. I take the days as they come. When they are gone, I am done with them," Achim said.

"Don't you hold onto the good days, bade Achim?" Oana asked.

"I don't cheat myself, Oana—even that way—what is gone is gone," Achim said.

"You have put on the clothes of old age and think you are dressed in your holiday best," Tudor said.

"You are wrong, Tudor. They grew on me. The years put them on me and I am not uncomfortable in them," Achim said.

For a man of seventy, Achim was hale and vigorous. His eyes were clear and his hair barely tinged with gray on the temples. He ate well, slept well, and worked well. And he was as strong as Tudor. One evening they wrestled, "without tricks" as he put it, and neither could throw the other.

Tudor was amazed. He felt the old man's arms, and Achim said, "It is all in the marrow, Tudor, and that you can't feel."

Tudor became bold and said, "But with women, bade Achim?"

"Now, that's a question, Tudor, you should ask men of your age so you could all brag together. For I must tell you, boy, at your age you do not know women. You are in the springtime of your life. Like in a tree, the sap flows strong in you. That is as should be. But the mind is as green as the leaves in spring. It can't judge. Myself, I had my spring, my summer, and now I feel autumn coming. It has not reached me yet though. But my mind is ripe. Do you understand what I am telling you, Tudor?" Achim said.

Tudor looked at Achim for a long moment. There was no evidence of comprehension in his eyes. Then suddenly he brightened, laughed, and said, "Long live springtime." The two younger shepherds burst into laughter.

97

They nudged one another and laughed. They were ogling Oana. She blushed.

The evenings when they sang and danced were much more interesting to me. That night I dreamed that Oana fell down from the attic, ladder and all.

Two days before we set out for home, I was sitting in front of the hut when I heard a woman's voice singing most dolefully. I had heard such bewailing at a funeral, when many women mourners were singing and lamenting. To hear this one voice in the middle of a bright summer day on a mountain plateau frightened me. I rose to run in as Oana was coming out of the hut. "Did you hear that, Peter?" she asked. I said I did. She took my hand and we walked in back of the hut. We saw approaching a woman leading a horse.

"You left me and our little ones, my dear husband. Woe is me, woe is me! There is no sun, there is no day or night for me. Only black sorrow. Woe is me, woe is me!" the woman chanted. Then she merely wailed. And as she trudged forward the horse followed her, its head bent low, as if it were overcome with sorrow. But now we could see that the horse was carrying a burden. It was a man. On one side of the horse his legs hung; on the other his head and arms.

"I loved him as the light of my eyes. My dear man, my good husband. He left me a widow, alone in the world, alone with my dark days. Oh-oh, oh! I have no more tears, my eyes are burned and my heart is broken," the woman chanted. She stopped and the horse stopped.

"Look at him, good people, look at him. He was my sweetheart and my husband, my man, ordained by God to be so, and the father of my children. Look at him, good people. Death, cruel death, took him from me in the prime of his life. Oh! Woe is me!"

"Come in and rest yourself, dear," Oana said, tears trickling down her cheeks.

"I will rest here, kind heart, I will not leave him alone. Oh, woe is me," the woman said, sobbing.

Oana rushed in and brought a stool from the hut. The woman dropped the end of the halter and reached up on the saddle where the dead man was. She untied a bundle that had lain crosswise on the back of the corpse. It was an infant, swaddled so it looked like a bundle of clothes. The little creature opened its eyes, yawned, and suddenly began to cry.

"Hush, hush, little one," the woman said. She sat down on the bench, opened her shirtwaist, and gave her breast to the infant. "Take it, the milk of your lonely mother, my poor fatherless orphan," she said. And looking up at Oana she said, "I hope, my dear, this sorrow has not turned the milk bitter in my breast. The poor little creature. His last child, my dear, and he still in the springtime of his life, green and strong as the oak. Four boys, the oldest a little man of eight. He could have given me as many daughters yet. Oh, woe is me."

The horse stood there, swishing the flies away with its long tail and stamping now one foot, now another. As it did so, the dead man's dangling head and legs swayed a little.

Oana brought out a jug of milk and corn bread and gave it to the woman. "God bless you with a long and happy life, dear," the woman said. She ate the corn bread and drank the milk, and the infant suckled, his tiny hand on the mother's breast. The rest of him, from below the armpits, was as stiff as a piece of wood in the tight swaddling.

"How did the misfortune come?" Oana asked compassionately.

"It came suddenly, dear, like lightning. I left my three little ones with their grandmother—his mother—dear, and came up with some corn meal, onions, and salt. He was repairing the hut. It had sagged at the foundation. He had dug under it and had the logs ready to put under the one corner that was up now on a piece of timber. His friend Gheorghe had helped him raise it, but he went out with the sheep. There he was in the hole when I arrived.

" 'You came in good time, Suzana,' he said, and laughed.

" 'Come out of that hole then,' I said, and laughed too.

" 'Soon. I have only to place these stumps here, make them solid,' he said. Then he bent down and dug a little more when suddenly the hut shook. 'Jump out,' I cried. He was bent over; the corner of the hut fell in on him and broke his back and his neck too. O God! How could You allow it? Why did the earth not open and swallow me? To see this calamity with my eyes! O God!" The woman rocked herself and started to wail. After a long moment she said, "I ran for Gheorghe. He heard my shrieking and came on the run. We got him out after much effort. He was dead. Oh, woe is me! I am taking him to be buried in hallowed ground, in our cemetery. God help me."

The infant had fallen asleep at his mother's breast. The horse stood there patiently. Flies were buzzing around the dead man's head. The woman rose. "I must be on my way, dear. The Lord repay you for your kindness," she said to Oana. She placed the infant on the dead man's back, fastened it with a long girdle, picked up the end of the halter, and walked off. She started to sing again her mournful dirge. "I am taking you, dear husband—Lord, my heart is heavy—to your resting place in the bosom of the earth. You are taking my happiness with you into the grave. Oh, woe is me!"

We watched her, Oana and I, and her voice came back to us fainter and fainter; then she vanished from sight after her voice could no longer reach us.

"Poor, poor woman," Oana said with a deep sigh. "Come, Peter. It is high noon. We will eat alone. The men will not return before sundown."

She set the table. There was milk, corn mush, and sweet cheese. Oana seemed in a hurry to have done with this. When everything was ready she said, "Come, dear, we shall send a prayer to God for the soul of the dead man and for his wife and children."

I kneeled down with her in front of the icon, the resurrection of Christ, and crossed myself three times as Oana did. Then she prayed. If I could have heard Oana's prayer I would have repeated the words after her. At length she said, "Amen," I repeated "Amen," and both of us made the sign of the cross three times.

"I have lightened my heart, dear," Oana said. She took me in her arms, kissed me on both cheeks, and we ate our midday meal. In the evening she told the story of the woman. The men listened somberly. Achim alone spoke. "Fate finds a man wherever he might be," he said.

On the eve of our departure, Uncle Gherasim made everything ready. Oana helped him. He stuffed one saddle bag with cheese, two small tubs of butter, and several packets of the fragrant gum which I had learned to chew.

101

These packets were made of bark from young fir. Then, as he was about to fasten the bag, Oana came from the cellar with a large piece of sweet cheese. "This is for my love, Peter," she said.

"So! He has taken your heart," Uncle Gherasim said.

"Yes. I gave it to him with both hands. You will cherish it, Peter dear," Oana said, embracing me. For answer I threw my arms around her neck and started to cry.

We left before sunrise, and this time my horse followed Uncle Gherasim's without being tied to it. I felt proud and happy. Several times I looked back. The hut and the pen appeared very lonely in the gray light of dawn. I felt a little sad leaving them. In one instant images came to my mind. Of my arrival there, of the bright days and cheerful evenings, of Oana, her singing and her fondling me.

We made good time, since the road descended gently most of the way, and the horses carried less weight than on the way to the mountains. We arrived home in the night. From the distance, the lights in the village looked like red stars.

"There it is," Uncle Gherasim said. We could hear the barking of far-distant dogs. As we approached the village some lights went out, and now the red stars had grown to square patches of light.

Our gate was fastened but Uncle Gherasim only knocked once before we heard running footsteps. Nicodin opened for us. In a moment mother and father came out.

Mother took the lantern from Nicodin and held it up to look at me. "My dear little soul. Oh, you are as black as a gypsy," she said and laughed, but I saw tears in her eyes.

Father took me off the horse. He kissed me and patted my back. Mother took my hand and said, "Come in, Uncle Gherasim, come please. Popa Radu told us you were coming today, but we were not certain." She reached up to feel my cheeks as we walked into the house, father carrying me.

Uncle Gherasim brought in the stuffed saddle bag. "We brought you a little present from the mountains," he said. Irina was sleeping and Maria too. I felt grown up and brave, coming home so late in the night from a long journey. But I fell asleep at the table while Uncle Gherasim had a glass of plum brandy with father, and never knew when he left. In the morning I woke up in my bed and the sun was shining in through both windows, it was so late. The door was being opened quietly and mother came in. "You are awake, my little soul," she said and rushed to me. "I came several times and you slept." She fondled me, pushed my head back on the pillow, raised me up and looked at me for a long moment. Then she said, "My beautiful, black son, you have really grown in this one month. My dear, dear little soul."

Irina came in. She smiled, then she laughed and opened big eyes. "Is he black, oh, so black, mother," she said. But she kissed me and I had to kiss her too. We both wiped our cheeks after this greeting.

I was home again. When mother asked me what I would like to have for breakfast I said I would like sweet cheese and milk.

⦿⦿⦿⦿⦿⦿⦿⦿⦿⦿⦿⦿

CHAPTER 12

"MEN ARE STRANGE BEINGS. AND MANY ARE THE ROADS
they travel, by God's good will." This was one of Uncle
Gherasim's favorite expressions. As a child at home, I
heard him say it, when teacher Vlad and father were discussing politics. Father always grew heated at these discussions. And he certainly would have thrown Vlad out
of the house but for the fact that he considered the teacher
a mere child in such matters. Then, too, father needed
somebody to whom he could talk politics, shouting and
banging on the table. Vlad was the right man for it because he would sit there blinking and if he got the chance
to say a word it would be so innocuous that father would
pass it off with a loud sniff.

Mother encouraged Vlad's visits. If father came home
all wrought up, the newspaper in his hand crushed, she
knew it was politics again. And she knew also that the
storm would break out as soon as father finished his dinner
and threw his napkin down. At such times we needed a
lightning rod. She would send Nicodin for the teacher.
Father never knew about mother's scheming. Nor did he

ever show surprise at Vlad's coming so opportunely. If it happened that he arrived while we were in the midst of our dinner, Maria would follow right behind him with plates and silver and set a place for him at table.

"Welcome, guest. Sit down with us, Vlad," father would say cheerfully. If Vlad had had his dinner already, father would make him have a second. "At your age, two meals can't hurt. Not at all," father would say. Generally, Vlad would eat as if he believed strongly that two meals could do no harm. Only, since he had come late, father would finish before him, and would fret a little waiting, and keep his napkin stuck in his vest to snatch it off directly after Vlad swallowed his last bite. Then he would pick up the rumpled paper and unfold it noisily saying, "The ungodly scoundrels are at their devilish tricks again," and finding the item he would slam the paper on the table in front of Vlad.

By this time mother would be walking quietly from the table, motioning to Irina and me to follow her. The door would remain open until Maria cleared the table, going in and out on tiptoe. She always looked relieved when she could finally close the door on the unpredictable room.

If Uncle Gherasim happened to come while Vlad and father were already closeted in the room, he would sit with us in the kitchen, which was large and more homey for Irina and me than all the other rooms. We could sit on the hearth and listen to mother and Uncle Gherasim chatting at the table and watch Maria do the dishes and put them away.

When father would raise his voice and bang the table, mother would glance at the closed door, as if expecting something to happen momentarily. Uncle Gherasim would then say, "Men are strange beings. And many are the roads they travel by God's good will."

These words always reassured mother. Smiling, she would answer, "We are strange indeed, Uncle Gherasim."

I asked Irina what is strange. She looked at me with her air of superiority and said, "Strange is like a stranger, what you don't know."

That was very stupid, I thought, because all men were men and I knew that. And if mother said we were all strange then she certainly did not mean we did not know each other.

Father told us once that most words were like a marketing bag. You put into it what you were able to purchase. Some people buy from life more than others, he said, so they put more meaning into words. And he said that you did not pay for these purchases with money but with something much more valuable, which was experience.

There was a great difference between him and mother. When he told us something he never asked if we understood what he said, while mother would always ask, "Do you understand?" and if I said no she would try to explain, giving us simple examples. She was very patient with us, but it was father who inspired my fancy. When he told us that experience was more valuable than money I tried to imagine what it could be. Then, because I heard Uncle Gherasim and mother say that health was more precious than anything I thought that experience was the same thing as health.

I said to Irina, "I know what you put in that marketing bag."

"What marketing bag?" she asked.

"The one father told us. Words," I said.

"Oh, words! What is it then you put in?" she asked with an air of challenge.

"You put in what you buy with health," I said.

"Oh, how silly!" she cried and started to laugh. "How silly," she kept repeating and laughing.

I often wished Irina was a boy so I would have an older brother like my friend Anton, the deacon's son. Anton was my age and his brother Simeon was eleven. Simeon was short and very strong and ran faster than all the boys of his age and even older. When his mother had laundry to take to the brook he wheeled the large basket of wet clothes in the wheelbarrow and, coming back, brought Anton sitting in it very proudly. His mother said that the girl who would marry Simeon would be the happiest wife in the world because Simeon had a heart of gold. I tried to imagine how Irina would be with a heart of gold but could not.

Simeon was like a mother to Anton. If he cried, Simeon wiped his tears with his own shirt sleeve and helped him blow his nose. He taught us to play ball, all children of our age, and never interfered in our game. But a great misfortune happened to Simeon. His hand was caught in the threshing machine and he lost all the fingers of the left hand except his thumb. His father consoled him, saying that would save him from serving three years in the army. "They are the best years in a man's life and he throws them away as if they were tattered shirts," he said. "And worse," Simeon's mother would add, "for whoever throws away a shirt no matter how tattered?"

࿐࿐࿐࿐࿐࿐࿐࿐࿐

CHAPTER 13

WHEN THE YOUNG MEN LEFT THE VILLAGE FOR THEIR military service it was a holiday, but a sad one. The parents and sweethearts accompanied them out of the village to the very far border of the communal land. This was the pasture land where the cows grazed from spring until the middle of autumn.

Of course the young men marched singing and the women sang with them too, but suddenly a girl's voice would break and then the women would raise their voices trying to drown the girl's weeping and wailing. At the point of parting the young men would kneel down, cross themselves, and kiss the ground saying, "We leave you with sadness in our hearts, beloved earth." Then they would embrace their dear ones and start off singing boisterously. Each year a few young men would leave for the army, but also others would return.

Father was angry at the government. He said it was a shameful waste taking the young men and keeping them for three years producing nothing and eating the fruit of the rest of the population's labor. "The imbeciles ought to know that one year is enough for these boys to learn how to carry a gun and how to fire it," he said. He wrote articles about this matter but since his cousin Silvestru Arin had fled, the newspaper would not print them. The editor would send them back with polite apologies which threw father in a rage. It was in one such outburst that he betrayed his secret to mother about his former contributions to the paper. "Silvestru had courage. He never sent back anything of mine. But this milksop has water in his veins," he shouted, throwing the packet of manuscript on the table.

"You did write for the paper, dear?" mother asked, surprised.

"Yes, Barbara. Now you know it," he said. Then he shouted, "Good Lord, and why not? I know what is right and what is wrong. And this military service is wrong. Wrong! Criminal!"

"But, dear, people are used to it. They take it for granted," mother ventured.

"People, people!" father shouted. "They have no voice, Barbara. I am their voice. Does the donkey take it for granted that he should be loaded mercilessly? Yes? And beaten, too, when he can no longer stand on his four legs? Do you know what he would say if he could talk? Do you? No! You do not. Then why say people take it for granted?"

"Of course, dear, if the donkey could speak . . ." mother would say and leave the room. We saw that she was blushing from the effort to hold back her laughter.

Father watched her, his right eyebrow raised. It was his way when puzzled and angry at the same time.

It really was dangerous for anyone to laugh in father's

presence when he was in one of his "passions," as mother called it. We did not know exactly what would happen but we firmly believed it would be terrible.

It happened of course when he was just normally irritated over something, nevertheless raising his voice, that mother would say a few words which justified her laughing and she did laugh. At such instances father would stare at her for a long moment, sniff noisily, and then say, "That is ridiculous, but not funny at all," and leave the room.

Mother said it was a blessing we had a garden and wood to be cut, because father sweated every kind of anger out of his system. Possibly that is why we stayed only a short time in the city.

When father was in one of his "passions" he would run out in his street clothes and start to work in the garden or cut wood. Then, as he got warm he would begin throwing off his clothes until he had nothing on but his underwear. One of us would then go out with his work pants and gather up his other clothes. He made believe he did not see what went on. We watched from the window. For a short time he would keep on at his labor, then suddenly throw down spade or ax and put on his pants.

Mother said there were only two men in the village at whom father never got angry and shouted—Uncle Gherasim and Andronic, the wheelwright. Yet nobody bore him a grudge. "He is like a father to us. He scolds us but he helps a man out of his trouble," the people said. With women he was simply curt; he never shouted at them. "Send your husband," he would say.

"I have no husband, domnule," a widow would say.

110

"Your brother, father, or grandfather. A man," father would say.

"I am alone like the cuckoo, domnule," the woman would say.

"So! Too bad. You are still young. Speak then," father would say. And he would listen with a degree of patience no man would suspect him of having.

Mother said that was the strongest proof that father had a heart of gold.

The work of a village notary is irksome. He keeps all the latifundian registers, the tax register, the cattle registers, and besides this he attends to legal matters such as contracts, acts as justice of the peace with the mayor in petty civil cases, and gives legal advice to people who must take their case to district courts.

And if he, like father, has the welfare of the people at heart, he actually gives his life to his work. That is what mother said of father. Because of this, mother tried with all her ability to make our home as pleasant as possible. She even closed her eyes to father's drinking. But not altogether. Periodically she would have what she called an earnest heart-to-heart talk with father about this. She would start in this manner:

"You are very full-blooded, dear. Really, your ears are like fire. Like hot coals. Of course, wine is good, but the best of anything can be harmful, can it not?"

"Yes, Barbara dear, the best of anything can be harmful, but wine is only good, as you say, and not the best of things," father would say with a short laugh.

"I am glad you agree, dear. It is not the best of things. That is exactly what I think but could not say it so well

111

as you. Therefore, maybe you could have just two glasses of wine with your breakfast. You see, dear, you have steak for breakfast. Meat is strong food, and too much wine with such food may be harmful."

"It could be, Barbara, to somebody who is not like me," father would say calmly.

"That is very good, but, dear, you have only one stomach, like everybody else," mother would say.

"Of course, else I would eat two steaks and drink two bottles of wine with breakfast," father would say still calmly.

"But I am serious. Let us not mention two stomachs, dear. You know that wine heats the blood and that makes you so impatient," mother would say.

"Now, Barbara dear, when am I impatient? When I am confronted with stupidity," father would say, less calmly.

"That is excusable. Stupidity is irritating. Only you are too quick to decide."

"Excusable! Quick to decide! To decide what, Barbara?" At this point father was no longer calm.

"To decide what is stupidity," mother would say. "Some people are merely slow but not stupid."

"Now, Barbara dear, I gave in to you about my having only one stomach. To please you, because we are not so sure about it. But when you want to teach me what stupidity is, that is too much," father would say.

"Then I shall say no more about stupidity, only about the wine," mother would say.

"My God, Barbara! How can you separate the two in this case? You said I lose my patience too quickly. I say I only lose it with stupidity. My drinking wine has nothing to do with my patience. Save me from stupid people

112

and I can drink thrice as much and be calm as a saint. And that's settled," father would say.

"Oh," mother would sigh. "I know what is good for you, dear, but I am not a lawyer."

This remark always angered father. He would get very red in the face, snatch open his shirt collar, take a few noisy breaths, and leave the room.

After a session like this mother would say nothing about father's drinking too much wine for a month or two, then she would bring it up again. Of course father always won out. If the truth be told, he actually drank more as time went on. He never got so inebriated that he would stagger like teacher Vlad for instance. But he would get very red in the face and his breath would smell like the vat in which they crushed the grapes for pressing.

CHAPTER 14

⊚⊚⊚⊚⊚⊚⊚⊚⊚⊚⊚⊚

OUR REGION HAD WONDERFUL VINEYARDS AND VERY
excellent grapes. The peasants understood viticulture and
tended their vineyards with especial care. The wheat and
grape harvests were occasions for joyous celebrations. But
as the grape harvest came later in the season and work on
the land was lessened, this could be celebrated more
leisurely. When the grapes were pressed the village was
redolent with the odor of the sweet juice from this "heavenly fruit," as father called it.

The mayor, Uncle Gherasim, and we closed the days of
grape harvest with feasting and music. Zunki, the cym-
balo player, and his three fiddlers played dance music or
folk tunes. The dance music "puts hot coals under your
feet," the peasants say, and Zunki and his fiddlers could
make a saint jump up and dance. But the folk tunes were
for the most part heartrendingly sad.

On the happiest occasion, the Romanian must have
some of this music. And he gives himself to sorrow and
gaiety with equal abandon. I have seen an expression of
rapture on the faces of peasants when they are listening

to the saddest music. Generally, when such music was played, one of the assembly would start to sing, then others would join in until everybody sang. The women would every now and again wipe the tears from their eyes as they sang. Mother sang too but whether she sang or not, she always wept.

Then suddenly Zunki would strike up a hora, or sirba, his hammers dancing over the wire strings. Instantly everybody would clap, rise, and dance.

Father was an excellent dancer and absolutely tireless. It was always he, Uncle Gherasim, and Andronic who danced last, the rest of the people clapping and stamping their feet. Then Andronic would drop out exhausted to be followed soon by Uncle Gherasim, leaving father alone in the middle of the floor doing intricate figures improvised on the moment.

On these occasions Irina and I were allowed to stay up until the end because mother would make us sleep several hours during the day. We too, children as we were, experienced the influence of the two forms of music. When the sad tunes were played and sung, Irina would sit in a trance, her eyes big with a sort of sorrowful wonderment, tears rolling down her cheeks. I never knew what was passing through her mind, what visions the melancholy strains evoked in her for, if I tried to speak to her at such moments, she pushed me away brusquely, not even glancing at me. No doubt she too was transported into a world of fancy which was more real to her than the actual. For my part, I saw myself in heroic action, freeing a beautiful fairy princess from dragons or from tyrannical parents and uniting her with her Prince Charming, their tears of gratitude wringing my heart and swelling it at the same time with a feeling of exaltation. In these states nothing was impossible of achievement. I was endowed with superhuman powers. In a flash I could transport myself from one end of the world to the other.

In Uncle Gherasim's stories the charmed horse would ask his master how he wished to be carried, with the speed of the wind or of thought. In my reveries I always traveled with the speed of thought. Sometimes I flew, as in dreams, passing over mountain peaks and large rivers and lakes whose borders were lost in infinity.

Then came suddenly the fiery dance music, breaking the spell with cruel harshness. The adults turned as suddenly from sadness to gaiety, but Irina and I, our dream world shattered, were dropped into the real world to flounder for a long spell like fish thrown on dry land.

Possibly mother also found more release in sad music than in gay. Her favorite folk songs were one more heartrending than the other. Father preferred the gay, the ribald, and the dance music.

In the winter we had one evening each week when women came to visit with mother, but not "with idle hands." They brought their distaffs and sewing. On these evenings father would leave the house after dinner to return when Irina and I had long ago gone to bed.

These were pleasant evenings. I liked especially to watch the women spin and listen to the purring of their spindles. And they talked about a woman's work, her endless duties in the home. They talked about children, about christenings, weddings, burials, and illnesses. They covered the whole range of life. They did not complain about their burden but took it to be a woman's lot in this life. "The Lord has made us so," they said, "we are peasants." This implied, of course, that their reward would come after they had passed on into another life. They believed firmly in an afterlife where they would have a reward consisting of eternal rest. When after a day's labor one is tired, restful sleep is welcome, so after a life of drudgery, eternal sleep in death is also welcome.

This does not mean, however, that the woman turned from life, that they in any way denied it. On the contrary, they gave themselves to it heart and soul. But they had no fear of death. Death was merely an exit from this life as birth was an entrance into it.

An expectant mother would say, "The Lord is giving us another child," the others answering, "May it come into this world hale and sound, to the happiness of its parents."

And if one had lost a child and came to mention it, she would say piously, if with sorrow, "The Lord has taken my dear Nicolai, he was the light of our eyes." The women would say, "The Lord gives us and He takes from us. He is our Heavenly Father, His name be blessed unto eternity."

There was a little gossiping too, and mother was not averse to it if it was merely news about what was going on in the village. That was why Chiva, the sharpest-tongued gossip, would spin "as one possessed" the women said when she was at our house. It was very trying for her having to keep out the spice from the mild gossip stew which the others were dishing out.

"I like to go there but it is penance I am doing in that house. You know what it means to keep your mouth shut when your tongue is burning," she told the women, who laughingly reported it to mother.

These gatherings of the women took place in our kitchen,

which was large and cozy. Then too, spinning requires a little spitting on the part of the spinner and the kitchen floor was considered by mother a better place for that purpose than the one in the sitting room. The spinner has to pick out kinks from the wool or hemp with her teeth and expel them from her mouth.

The large ceiling lamp hung over the table so the women who did sewing sat there. The spinners sat on the bench against the wall or on the hearth bench. These latter had the advantage of spitting out what they picked from the thread into the fire on the hearth.

I liked to sit on the end of the hearth bench and watch these women, but Irina always sat at the table because mother wanted her to learn sewing and embroidery. She was clever with the needle but liked crocheting best of all. She made enormous lengths of lace of one kind or another for which there was never enough use. Then she would undo what remained and crochet something that had immediate use.

On such evenings I alone sat with idle hands until mother brought in walnuts for everybody. Then she gave me a flatiron and a small hammer and I would crack the nuts and fill a large wooden bowl from which the women helped themselves. Besides nuts there would be apples and dry prunes on the table, but for drinking, only water, not like when men came. They were served plum brandy or wine.

These were all married women, wearing the customary turban that covered the head entirely. A married woman is never seen bareheaded by men other than her husband. The greatest offense to a married woman is to have her headgear snatched off by someone.

It happened sometimes that two women would quarrel in the street. If they lost their tempers to the point of rushing at each other, the struggle would be for the head covering. If one succeeded in exposing the other's head, the one with a bare head would either burst into tears or fly into a wild rage and pursue her adversary until she escaped in her house behind bolted door.

Only once did we actually see this happen. It was Chiva, the gossip, who quarreled with one of her neighbors as they were coming from the mill, each carrying a bag of flour on her shoulder. It was in the late afternoon on a Saturday. The street was already swept clean. They walked along side by side, jabbering, when suddenly Chiva threw down her bag. The other woman lost no time. She set down her bag too and they flew at each other. Chiva had the advantage. She snatched the turban off the other woman's head, grabbed up her bag, and ran. The bareheaded woman cried out, "The witch," and chased her, with both hands covering her head. Chiva escaped by running into her yard and bolting the gate. They became mortal enemies.

Mother was a peacemaker. The women loved and respected her. They abided by her decision in cases of differences, which they brought to her. But she never succeeded in making peace between Chiva and the offended woman.

"I am bad in anger but there is no evil in me. The Lord is my witness, I bear her no ill," she said to mother.

"Then go and ask her forgiveness," mother said.

Chiva grew pale. She said she could not do it. The woman would tear her eyes out, she said. This was perhaps not true because mother spoke to the other woman who said, "I will never harm that witch, but never will I forgive her. Let her go to her grave with the sin on her soul."

It grieved mother to know that such enmities existed. She could not understand why human beings could not settle their differences and forgive injuries. She used to say that to forgive is a virtue. Forgiveness unburdens one's heart, she said. She always brought up the Lord's Prayer and said that we can only gain forgiveness for our transgressions if we forgive and bear no grudge against others.

Father agreed with her about forgiving, but he insisted on due punishment first.

"But, dear, what do you forgive if you punish?" mother asked.

"That is very simple, Barbara," father said. "We must pay for our deeds, must we not?"

"Yes, we do pay for our deeds," mother agreed.

"Well then, punishment is the pay. Then comes forgiveness," father said.

That was too much for mother. And it was all wrong too she said, but father stuck by his guns. He simply would not do away with just punishment. He said that forgiveness had value only because punishment existed. We knew forgiveness because we knew punishment. Punishment could exist without forgiveness but not forgiveness without punishment.

To all this mother said that father could make out that black is white and seem plausible, but that was only because he was so clever and at any rate cleverness had absolutely nothing to do with forgiveness. This comes from the heart, she said.

Father was ready to take up the subject from this point too, but mother said no. And so we children had both punishment and forgiveness, because, as mother told me, I should never forget that we all have two parents.

CHAPTER 15

⊙⊙⊙⊙⊙⊙⊙⊙⊙⊙⊙⊙

THE PEASANT MISTRUSTS INTELLECTUALS BECAUSE
he does not understand them. He feels that the burden of
making himself understood is on the man who pretends to
have learning. "What you have clear in your mind you
can tell simply without getting into clouds of words," he
says.

Andronic had a nephew, Liviu Sabin, a pompous young
man who studied law. He would come to the village "to
remake his blood," as Andronic used to say. "He comes
from the city pale as a ghost as if the sun never shone on
him."

Now, this Liviu Sabin was a great talker. There was
nothing under the sun that he did not pretend to know.
If the people worried about lack of rain he knew exactly
why it did not rain. And he would talk about it at great
length, using terms like meteorology, astronomy, oxygen,
hydrogen—whatever came "on his tongue."

The men listened to him but made nothing of what he
said. But they knew one thing, the earth needed rain. So
after Liviu finally stopped jabbering an old man would

122

say, "Lord, how beautifully you talk. Yes indeed. Now we must know why the rain does not come. But tell us, Liviu, what shall we do to get rain? For you see, Liviu, we need the rain much more than the knowledge why it does not come."

"Yes, I can see that," Liviu would say, "but everything has two ends, the negative and the positive. Once you know the negative you come to the positive on wings. Absolutely. The universe is governed by laws. Every law has in it the negative and the positive. You must never forget that. Always keep in mind the negative and the positive. But then comes the crucial point, the great question—is there really a negative or only a positive in the laws of nature? The answer is yes and no! The positive is there, absolutely—the world could not exist without it—but the negative is a conception of man. The negative exists in his mind, the positive exists in nature. This is an axiom, a self-evident truth. Now what is a self-evident truth? A self-evident truth is something that *is* and cannot be denied."

"Like this lack of rain," the old man put in quickly.

"Oh, no! Not like that. The lack of rain here, on this spot of the earth, is a relative truth," Liviu said. And from that point he had easy sailing. He left the rain in the hands of God and talked about the relative.

I remember when I heard Liviu Sabin hold forth in this manner for the first time. It was a Sunday and I sat by Uncle Gherasim in front of his house. The two long benches were occupied by men, sitting and listening to Liviu. He spoke a long time, standing in front of us, his chest out and most of the time looking above our heads.

123

Now and again he would take a step forward, then a step back, as he talked.

At long last, Liviu pulled out his watch, glanced at it, and said, "Sorry, I must go now. My books are calling to me. So much work." He ran off.

When he got out of earshot the old man said, "Well, Gherasim, we are enlightened." He chuckled. Then everybody laughed. Andronic said, "We have to admit that we can learn from this nephew of mine."

"What do we learn, Andronic?" asked the old peasant.

"We can learn the negative. Wait, don't laugh. We learn not to have our minds darkened as he has his," Andronic said.

"Andronic is right," Uncle Gherasim said. "These fellows never learn enough to know that man is more than all knowledge. So they put knowledge way above man and then everybody looks small to them, including themselves. To cover their smallness they strut about like peacocks, all puffed up. Now, the peacock has lovely feathers, pleasing to the eye, but the pride of these braggarts is as becoming to them as a big goiter."

They became serious. For a while no one spoke. Then the old peasant said, "Still, Gherasim, knowledge is good. If a man knows how to work his field it is good. If he can read and write, it is good."

"Certainly knowledge is good. It is a tool in man's hands; only a tool to be used by him. But when he makes of it something holy that he worships, then he is blind," Uncle Gherasim said. The peasants nodded their heads in agreement.

Uncle Gherasim had a great gift at illustrating graphically his statements. He never lost patience with silly people but made every effort "to make them understand what troubles them," he put it. "For there are people," he said, "who burden themselves with all kinds of troubles which most of the time is fog in their minds. A man will put on clean clothes on holidays and he will sweep his house clean, yet never thinks that his thoughts need cleaning too. Such a man is like one who goes through his days in soiled and tattered clothes."

Sometimes the young priest Filimon, on a visit to Popa Radu, would soar into the thin air of rhetoric, preaching with the permission of his host. The peasants would come out of church baffled, for they understood nothing of his sermon. At such times the men would gather around Uncle Gherasim and ask what the priest had meant. One such Sunday father and I had met Uncle Gherasim in the street. Several men came up to us, then more gathered, and we stopped. They asked Uncle Gherasim about the sermon. "We could not follow him," one peasant said.

"No, we could not, that is true," several voices said in chorus.

"Well," Uncle Gherasim said, "this priest is young. He does not yet know that to fly you need wings, and the best wings a man can have are good common sense."

"And the air in which his wings can hold him up is sound knowledge," father said. "Very true," the men said.

It was because father helped the peasants with his knowledge of law that they respected him so highly. He was their ideal of a learned man. And of course, he never would muddle their heads talking to them of things he knew nothing about, like this Liviu Sabin or the young priest.

There were cases when, because he was so trusted, a

peasant would come to father and ask him for advice about his wife's illness. "We have tried everything, but the poor woman is wasting away on her feet. She bore us four sons and three daughters, all healthy, then one day she complained of a pain in her side and her back. The women gave her now this, now that to drink, brewed from all sorts of herbs and roots. Nothing helped. They tried incantations and even sorcery, for it could be the evil one. Nothing helps. That is why I come to you, humbly to ask what we could do for her. It breaks our hearts. She looks more dead than alive and the pain never leaves her, yet she never complains, only when she thinks nobody can hear, the poor woman groans pitifully, and we make believe we do not hear because she wants it so. She thinks of us, of me and of the children, she is the light in our home, but now the light is going out, domnule. May the good Lord bless you, help us."

It was Filimon Bucur who spoke to father in these words. He sat bowed, his eyes resting imploringly on father. Mother had tears in her eyes and I walked quietly to the far corner of the room and cried. Only Irina sat by father, leaning against him, his arm about her shoulder, and looked at the man spellbound.

Father listened to the man, then he said very quietly, "Filimon, I wish God had given me the wisdom to help you. But I have not that wisdom. And I have not the knowledge of a doctor either. So, Filimon, all I can do is call my brother, the doctor. I will send for him. If he can, he will help you."

The man sighed, rose from his chair, and said, "May it be in a good hour, domnule. I have come to you with hope and with good hope I leave you in God's care." He picked up his hat from the floor and left.

The poor woman had cancer on the liver. Uncle Alexander told us there was no hope for her. She died two months later.

Father had great confidence in the sciences. He admired Uncle Alexander, who was reputed as a keen diagnostician. But when they spoke about it, Uncle Alexander said that medicine was still in its infancy and he did not scorn the home remedies the peasants used. As to diagnosis, he said one could not learn it at medical schools. A young doctor was not as well equipped for his calling as an engineer or a chemist, for instance, he said.

"Then how does he become a reliable diagnostician?" father asked.

"That is a difficult question," Uncle Alexander said. "Perhaps the man who gets to be a reliable diagnostician has the qualities of a keen detective. Do not scoff at this. Symptoms can be as misleading as circumstantial evidence. A fever, pain in some part of the body, are symptoms. But of what? I had a case. The patient, a woman, had high fever. I had to do something to reduce her temperature. What caused it I did not know. When I saw her the following day, her temperature was exactly where I had found it. Yes, I was told, after she took what I prescribed the temperature diminished a little, then it flew up again. I was absolutely at a loss what to do. Let her take the same medicine, I advised. The following day I arrived several hours later than I had intended, because I had had two urgent calls. The sick room smelled horribly of onions. The patient was no longer delirious. Her temperature was normal. But what was this smell of onions? This is what I was told. A friend of the family, an old peasant woman, came to visit them soon after I had left the previous day. 'This fever must be stopped at once. The poor dear is burning up,' the woman said. She asked for onions, a lot of onions. She chopped up the onions and stuffed a thick layer of them in large woolen stockings which were put on the patient. Then she put chopped onions in the stockings all around the legs up to the knees and fastened the stockings. This was done in the early afternoon. The morning of the following day the fever was practically gone. When I arrived, the patient had no trace of it. What caused the fever I do not know. The old peasant woman watched me take the temperature of the patient. A kindly person she was. She sat there, her earnest eyes on me, like a mother watching her child at its play. I turned to her and said, 'Tell me, what caused this great fever? Do you know?'

" 'No, sir, I do not know. It is a fire in the body. God alone knows how it comes. But I know that such fire is dangerous. Must be quenched. Our body is like a house. If it takes fire it burns until the fire is put out. More I do not know, sir,' the woman said.

" 'But about the onions. How did you know they would help?' I asked.

" 'Forgive me, sir, but we simple folk know what we learn, child from parent, from the beginning of the world. That is how we know the virtue of the onion. It has many virtues, sir,' the woman said.

"There you have it, brother," Uncle Alexander said. "Now, am I going to prescribe chopped onions in cases of stubborn fever? I shall be branded for a quack if I do.

Still, I shall try it yet—on some good friend." He laughed.

We could see that father was impressed because it was Uncle Alexander who told him this onion story. Possibly also because he has always considered the onion, garlic too, as vegetables without which humanity would have a much poorer culinary art. They started a conversation on the excellence of the garlic and the onion.

"Why the devil does not everybody eat garlic and onions every day so we would not be offensive when we eat it?" father said. "When I have to go to the city, for two days Barbara keeps these good things from me. I suffer, Alexander! And for what?"

"For civilization, I would say," Uncle Alexander said. "I know how you object to the smell of tallow."

"It is not the same thing," father protested. "Tallow on a peasant's feet. Ugh!" he made a grimace. "But garlic, onion, they are a gift from heaven. Maybe a good part of their virtue is in their smell."

"I don't know, I have never studied that. In any case, why could nature not give them the fragrance of roses or violets?" Uncle Alexander said.

"Because nature knows better," father said. "Would you like a roast leg of lamb smelling of roses or of violets? And what about sausage?"

Then they went into a long discussion about foods, about cooking, about the people who have developed this art to the highest, agreeing and disagreeing, until they decided that Romanian cooking was on a par with the best and mother had no rival as a cook.

This led Uncle Alexander to the subject of pellagra, which he had studied extensively. He had a strong rival, a renowned bacteriologist whose contention was that pellagra was caused by moldy or otherwise contaminated corn. Corn is a staple food with the Romanian peasant despite the fact that Romanian wheat is excellent. But because wheat has a greater market value, the peasant sells his wheat and feeds himself on corn. Uncle Alexander maintained that pellagra was not caused by bacteria, it was a disease caused by poor economy—corn had not sufficient food value for the human body. He proposed that the government open kitchens in the rural districts where cases of pellagra were found and supply the people with the required food elements, at the same time instructing the housewives how to balance the daily rations of nourishment. This involved some expenditure, of course, and the government accepted rather the contention of the bacteriologist. "Let the peasants eat corn, they are used to it, but let them not eat moldy corn," was the decision it took. It was the easy way out for it, and the "great authority"—the bacteriologist—helped to wash its face, not its hands, and the funds for "trying a hypothetical experiment," as the politicians put it, remained in the coffers of the secret funds, from where they could flow as the party in power directed.

Uncle Alexander had fought for many years against the "stupidity and inhuman arrogance" of the bacteriologist, but he was only a physician while the other was a member of the Academy and a recognized scientist. He spent his own and his wife's fortune studying pellagra in the various parts of Europe. He was bitter against the unpatriotic attitude of the government and considered the bacteriologist his greatest enemy as well as the enemy of the people.

To "pacify him," so the men in power put it, his book

on pellagra was awarded the Academy prize, a few thousand lei, and published under its imprint. This is supposed to be a great honor. But Uncle Alexander wrote a scathing article in which he said that the politicians followed the bug and got in the dung heap, which was where they belonged. The bug was the bacteriologist, of course. The result was that he lost his chair at the university, despite the protest of the medical students.

He was branded as a rebel. Then it happened that an old statesman whom he admired became seriously ill. The family had the best doctors, who, after consultation, decided that the man could not be saved. As a last resort, the family called Uncle Alexander. When he came, the bishop was at the patient's bedside to administer the last holy communion.

Uncle Alexander chased him out. If it was a matter of attending to the sick man's soul, the bishop could do it wherever he pleased. The physician's duty was to care for the body so it was his place to be at the man's bedside. This procedure brought the Church against him too, but Uncle Alexander scored against it and against the medical pundits. He saved the patient.

This gave him the reputation of being an eminent physician, although his manner was brusque. "But in case of need one has to put up with a man's eccentricities," one paper said. That gave Uncle Alexander the opportunity to come back at the politicians. He wrote a long article in which he said that results counted. He could not—as a physician—allow his patients to die, while the churchmen stole precious time with their mummery, just as the politicians steal time with their silly speeches, leaving a large number of the population helpless against pellagra, covering their gross unconcern with the affirmations of a man who defies the word science with his abysmal ignorance.

After this he was branded as a godless rebel. The priests took up arms against him. How dared he call the high function of the priest mummery? Where would the people be without the spiritual guidance of the church? Is religion mummery? This physician is an enemy of the state. He is attacking it at its very foundation. He is trying to lead the faithful believers back into the darkness of heathenism. So the papers wrote.

Uncle Alexander had to defend himself. He came back against the Pharisees with no less a champion than Christ. "I am no more against righteousness and the welfare of man than the Savior was," he wrote. "Christ healed the sick and drove the devil out of those possessed. I am dedicating my life to healing the sick. As to chasing out the devils, that I leave to God. It is beyond my power to cope with them. They are legion," he wrote. "I am not against the ethical principles of religion. We are taught to do unto others as we would have others do unto us. Do the politicians follow this? Let them search into their hearts." And again he brought up the subject of pellagra. From this he had a wide avenue open to the conditions of the peasantry. To social injustice, to the poverty of large numbers of peasants, and the ill-gotten opulence of the landowners who enslave the peasant.

Of course, his few friends stood by Uncle Alexander, but the landed gentry became his mortal enemies. The outcome was that he got a clientele from the poor classes large enough to keep a score of physicians busy day and night. Poor Uncle Alexander became a martyr. He tried

132

to raise money for a hospital for the poor but the money was in the hands of his enemies.

Mother admired Uncle Alexander greatly. "He is a saint," she said. "Yes," father said, "but this world is cruel to saints."

Mother sighed because she firmly believed that father also was sacrificing his life to the peasants, not quite like a saint, but still with enough devotion to earn him a little halo. And she was sure that both Uncle Alexander and father would be rewarded in some way for their good deeds, the first prize going to Uncle Alexander, of course.

But then, Uncle Alexander had no children and his profession was more lucrative than father's. Possibly, therefore, father was quite as deserving as his brother, because if he lost patience easily that was understandable. His burden was heavier. She firmly believed that ours is a just God and wise, and the world is ruled by Him with utmost justice and highest wisdom.

There was, to be sure, the old peasant saying that before you reach God the saints will devour you, but mother gave this saying the proper place. That applied, she said, in worldly matters, to men, not to God and the saints. For certainly the saints would under no circumstances behave counter to God's wishes.

Men of importance, such as high officials, are surrounded by underlings who usually fleece a petitioner trying to reach their chief. Besides, these high personages were of a kind with their underlings.

She was sorry that the clergy had risen against Uncle Alexander because her faith in it was shaken. The priests were only human, she said; still, being anointed, their duty was to take sides with the righteous. We had several friends in the priesthood whom mother respected and was fond of. One was Popa Radu, a man among the best of men, she said.

⊙⊙⊙⊙⊙⊙⊙⊙⊙⊙⊙⊙⊙

CHAPTER 16

POPA RADU REIGNED SUPREME IN HIS COMMUNITY.
A powerful man, gifted with a voice like thunder and a
healthy appetite, he was intelligent, with a great sense of
humor and mischief, too.

His visits to us were holidays for mother. She was kept
laughing all the time by his stories.

In a village the priest, the notary, and the teacher rep-
resent the spiritual and temporal light. Their advantage
over the peasant consists in the fact that they are specialists: the priest in regard to clerical matters, the notary in
affairs of law, and the teacher in education. They are
respected by the peasant as specialists in their fields.

But the peasant has his own culture—his lore, his prov-
erbs, his customs. Of course, religion is an integral part
of his ethics. But the peasant's religious beliefs do not entirely correspond to theological doctrines. He is close to
pantheism. He believes that the spirit of God is in everything. He also believes that the devil worms his way into
some things—now and again—and in man too. And he
has his superstitions.

135

The peasant allows for human weakness in these men, especially in the priest. He says, "Do as the priest tells you but do not do as he does." Of course he is much closer to the priest than to the notary and the schoolteacher. After all, the priest can help his soul.

A priest like Popa Radu is a boon, for he is a great factor in the life of the community. To begin with he is an expert farmer. He knows remedies against blights of corn, garden plants, and fruit trees. He gets pamphlets from the agricultural experimental laboratories, asks the advice of men at the agricultural college, and corresponds with supervisors of great estates.

And he is a powerful man, bursting with health. And a great worker. "He drives the laziness out of you, and just to look at him mowing or pitching hay makes you feel ashamed to lag behind," the peasants of our village say. "A man from God he is."

"When such a priest comes to a sick person he brings health with him, not a reminder of one's end," they say.

One day Simeon, the grave digger, suddenly fell ill. The pain in his back was so cruel he groaned all the time. The women sent for Popa Radu. Uncle Gherasim was there when the priest arrived. And he did not bring his peplum and other things that a priest carries to a dying man. He came from the field smelling of freshly mown hay.

"You want me, Simeon? What ails you?" Popa Radu asked the man.

"The pain is everywhere, your reverence," the man said, and groaned.

"That's good. You get rid of it in one piece," Popa Radu said.

"It may be the end, your reverence, I am close to seventy," the man said.

"How old was your father when he died?" Popa Radu asked.

"He was eighty-seven, may the Lord rest his soul in peace," the man said.

"And your mother, Simeon, how old was she?" Popa Radu asked.

"She, God rest her soul, might have been the same age, she died six years later," Simeon said.

"So! And you talk about your end. That's a sin, Simeon. You cannot shame your parents dying at your age. You are not through with your allotted work in this world. The Lord does not call you before you have done your work. And this thing about the pain being everywhere in you. You know what that is, Simeon? It is exhaustion. Fatigue. Nothing more. How long since you took to bed, Simeon?"

"This is the sixth day, your reverence," Simeon said.

"You need more days to rest. That is what you need, Simeon. More rest. Think to yourself, 'I am resting to get over this fatigue.' Keep that thought in your mind. You will get well, Simeon," Popa Radu said. Then he made the sign of the cross over Simeon and left. Uncle Gherasim walked to the gate with him. "Give him two or three raw eggs with a few drops of plum brandy. He might be a little starved too," he said to Uncle Gherasim.

They never knew what had ailed Simeon but they fed him with raw eggs and plum brandy and with rich sour milk. In a week Simeon was up. All his aches had left him.

"I will not say that Popa Radu performed a miracle, but he helped Simeon to get well, and by putting the right thoughts in his mind, nothing else. That is wise, for

137

if he had let Simeon think it was his end he might have poisoned himself with that thought and died," Uncle Gherasim said, adding, "You see, man, like fish, starts to spoil at the head."

Popa Radu, like father, helped his authority in worldly matters considerably with his physical strength. For when it comes to judging wool, or hemp, or lumber, for instance, the priest is no more qualified for the work than any other man, simply because he is anointed. Yet, if Popa Radu said, "This is the best wool grown on any sheep," and saying so he thrust the bundle under your nose, you agreed with him. It was safer.

This does not mean that he abused his authority too much, for he was a good-hearted man. But then he was human. In cases of small differences between his and another man's opinion, Popa Radu saw no wrong in swinging the scales in his favor by merely taking a deep breath that swelled his huge chest impressively and with it blasting out the words, "It is as I say."

Nobody wondered at the reputation of these two men, Popa Radu and father, from his first encounter with them. Of course father's reputation was the result of his cleverness in matters of law, and also his shrewdness with the cunning. He always played along with a sly man, but it was he who marshaled the game. For instance, take the time when I was ten years old and father had me in his study to copy some papers.

A short, fat peasant, dressed in his Sunday clothes, came into the room. Father had answered "enter" to the knocking on the door. He came from another village. He was the richest man there and the stingiest. His complaint was against a poor man, one Vasile Toma, who had seen father a few days earlier because he was threatened with a law suit by the rich peasant.

Father looked up from his desk and motioned to the fat man to come nearer and sit down. "Now, what brings you to me?" he asked.

"The wickedness of people, sir, brings me to you," the man began. He made his complaint at great length; at times tears came to his eyes as he wondered how the good earth can bare so much wickedness. Father, who usually snapped at long-winded talking, allowed this man to "empty himself."

Then he said, "Your name is Avram Tudorel. Yes, you told me. And the man whom you accuse of stealing your wheat is Vasile Toma. You say his land borders on yours?"

"Yes, sir, that is true, and a poor patch of land it is, very poor, so his wheat is always poor too, while mine is always good," Avram said.

"How do you know he stole your wheat?" father asked.

"Very easily, sir. I own the threshing machine, so I feed the sheaves to it myself because I know how better than others. I thresh everybody's wheat in my village. Those who have much have the machine brought to them, the others bring the wheat to me. I have a big yard. Vasile bought two heavy loads. I was up on the thresher. Vasile came up too, his work being to untie the sheaves and hand them over for me to feed the thresher. Now, the sheaves kept coming up, all the same poor kind of wheat, as it always came from Vasile's field. Then suddenly I got my hands on the other kind, the finest; the straw long, the spears heavy, wheat exactly like my own. 'This is my property,' I said to myself. To Vasile I said nothing. The thresher was going, the men threw the sheaves to Vasile, and he, all red in the face, watching me, so I decided to let him be and have the court give me justice. Now I come to you, sir, because you are known as a good lawyer and not too expensive and, you know us peasants, who are simple folk as the Lord made us," Avram said.

"Could you swear that this wheat which you claim was yours is indeed yours?" father asked.

"Indeed, sir, I could swear, by the evidence of my eyes," Avram said.

"But is there not much dust up where you stand, feeding the threshing machine?" father asked.

"Dust there is, sir, plenty, but I am used to it," Avram said, blinking fast. He sensed the import of the question.

"And you do get dust in your eyes?" father asked.

"A little dust does get in the eyes; truth is truth, and I never deny the truth," Avram said.

"Then you would swear that the wheat was of two kinds?" father asked.

"That I would, sir, on my good luck," Avram said.

"Tell me, Avram, did you sell Vasile Toma two sacks of your wheat in the past winter?" father asked.

"Well, sir, you might call it that in a way, but actually, as we know selling and buying, that it was not. The way it was is that Vasile worked for me a number of days, cutting wood and hauling it from the forest into my yard. There he cut it up in proper lengths for use in the house and stacked it up under a shed. 'What do I owe you, Vasile?' I asked him, out of the goodness of my heart. I knew well what his work was worth. But what does he say without blushing? He says, 'Three sacks of wheat.' 'Never, Vasile! Never! Three sacks of wheat? Never!' I said.

"So we started haggling, by which I mean he did, be-

140

cause I only repeated, 'Two sacks is more than ample for the work you have done.' He gave in, measure by measure, until he said, 'Take the heart out of me too, with my sweat, you godless usurer.' He took the two sacks of wheat and went away angry, but not before he insulted me in the presence of my wife and children. He said, 'May the good Lord award your labor as you are paying me for mine.'"

"Vasile had two sacks of your wheat then," father said.

"Which he and his family ate up during the winter. He has six children," Avram said.

"And how do you know that?" father asked.

"Well, sir, according to him, he more than earned it. He complained against my payment, angrily. Therefore he certainly would want to eat up the wheat before he touched his own, which is poorer. That is natural in my judgment," Avram said.

"Could you swear that Vasile and his family ate up the two sacks of wheat during the winter?" father asked.

"Sir, do you ask could they eat that much? If that is your question sir, I say yes, I could swear to it," Avram said.

"No! That is not my question. I ask you, could you swear that they ate up the two sacks of wheat?" father said.

"This question, sir, has another hue; that I must admit. Still, by the evidence of my judgment I can say yes, by this evidence I could swear," Avram said.

"Very well, Avram, but your judgment cannot be a witness for you in court. Your judgment means no more before the judge than your hat. You see, Avram, Vasile did not consume the wheat. He kept it for seed to sow in the spring. The proof of it is that he harvested what he sowed," father said.

Avram blinked rapidly. He seemed at a loss but he soon recovered. He scratched his head a little and then he said, "Sir, we have on the one hand my judgment, by which I could swear, as I said; on the other hand we have the wheat. Now, putting one against the other which is stronger?" he asked.

"Tell me, Avram, how much of your kind of wheat would you say Vasile harvested?" father asked.

"I would say, sir, ten or twelve sacks. Let it be ten," Avram said.

"There is your answer, Avram. You place the wheat above your judgment. You have no case against Vasile Toma. But you have taken my time. I will not ask you to pay me money. Two sacks of your wheat will do," father said.

Avram picked up his hat from the floor, arose, and said, "When it comes to legal matters I get tangled. So, I will pay. But I will be very busy with the end of summer work. Could you please wait a few weeks for the payment? Then I will bring it, two sacks of wheat," Avram said.

"I shall make it easy for you, Avram. Give the two sacks of wheat to Vasile. I will settle with him," father said.

"If so, let it be so. I will give Vasile the wheat," Avram said and left. In his village he told to all who would listen, that this "notary-lawyer"—meaning father—mixed up the thoughts in his head so he could not see white from black.

"He got me all tangled up in my own words until I was like a fish on dry land. And even now I do not know if I had a case against Vasile or not. Maybe that is why everybody says this notary is a great lawyer. He takes from one and gives to another," Avram said.

But the peasants knew him. His story increased their

confidence in father. And as the story was being told and retold, the fee he had paid father grew from two sacks of wheat to eight, for which everybody who knew Avram was glad.

We had in our village a man of Avram's kind. He also was a miser and was well to do. He was younger than Uncle Gherasim so he tried year after year to get ahead of Uncle Gherasim with the work on the land. He believed that gaining time against the man who was held to be the best farmer in the district would be of profit to him. If, for instance, he took in the corn two or three days earlier than Uncle Gherasim, he could prepare the land and do his winter sowing that much earlier too. He would bring in wood for the winter earlier, and so be all along a few days ahead of Uncle Gherasim. In other words, he would be richer with that many days.

But to achieve this the fellow had to drive himself mercilessly because Uncle Gherasim was very methodical. Then too, he was clever at reading the signs of the weather. The skies might be clear in the early morning but if you could "smell rain in the breeze," like Uncle Gherasim, you would not start cutting the wheat. This miser of ours, Ivan Gorun, was often fooled by the weather, so they nicknamed him *Proroc,* which means Prophet. Nevertheless, Proroc gained two or three days on Uncle Gherasim in the course of a year, only how prove it? Well, Proroc boasted of having found a way. He kept a record of the wheat harvest, the plowing for winter sowing, and providing wood for the cold season. And so if he was one day ahead of Uncle Gherasim at each of these labors, he set down three days to his credit.

How this racing of his became known was an accident.

It happened during the plum harvest. One of Uncle Gherasim's goats got into Proroc's orchard and was caught eating plums from the trees. That was an outrage, for there were enough plums on the ground. Proroc threw a heavy club at the goat and broke one of its hind legs. He would have denied his deed had not one of his men seen it. So he sent word to Uncle Gherasim to come for his "straying, destructive beast."

Uncle Gherasim sent his helper, Anton. "Where is the creature?" Anton asked.

"The creature is here, where it had done me more damage than it is worth, dead or alive, but where is your master?" Proroc asked.

"He is at his own affairs. I came for the goat," Anton said.

"You came for the goat! You came for the goat! Did you bring the ransom?" Proroc said heatedly.

"So the creature is held for ransom? Well now! And what is the ransom you want?" Anton asked.

"Enough to pay for the damage. Tell your master I want him to come. He can judge for himself," Proroc said.

"He has no time. And he will not come for the goat, because he sent me and it is my duty to take the goat. Where is it?" Anton said.

"I want my money first, for the damage," Proroc said.

"So! You refuse to free the goat! Suppose it dies. Well? And, I have a thought. Maybe the goat is dead," Anton said, "else you would show it to me."

Proroc turned pale. Gherasim was not the man to arouse. He was respected by everybody and to have his enmity meant to have the whole village against you. Of course the accursed goat did damage to one or two small trees, but to break its leg—that upset everything. Proroc thought best to speak to Anton reasonably and win him to see his side of the affair.

"Listen to me, Anton. We all have faults, but we are good Christians. There is only one God, and we are all His children. Now take Gherasim and take me. Is there any difference between us excepting that I am younger? No! But this difference is to my advantage because, as you know, I get ahead of him in my work and so I gain days against him. Not many, no, but any gain is so much to the good. Then also . . ."

"Wait a little, Proroc. What are you talking about? I came for the goat, that is all. What you think and what a good Christian you are does not bring the goat where it belongs. Let me have the goat and you settle with Gherasim," Anton said.

"Don't lose your patience, Anton, the goat *is* at the bottom of all this. And an old creature it is too, with brittle bones like dry twigs. A beast like that can break its legs very easily and . . ."

Anton cut in, "And the goat broke its legs, you want to say. What I say is, show me the goat this instant or go to the devil."

"Look here, Anton, what kind of behavior is this? I am the loser, so I should be the insulted too? In my own place? Suppose the accursed goat has a broken leg, did I bring it in my orchard? Am I to take care of Gherasim's animals?" Proroc said.

"Now, I understand you. The goat has a broken leg. Did you break its leg, tell me that, everything else you did tell me," Anton said.

"Do not play the clever, Anton, I know what I told you

145

and what I did not tell you. You are not Gherasim. But you came for the goat and the goat caused me damage. Causing me damage it got a broken leg. How it happened is nothing to bother about. One goes with the other—damage to me, broken leg to the goat. What you must see, Anton, is that I am the injured party. The damage is to me. That is what I want you to see, Anton. To see right, for the good of your soul, and tell Gherasim that I am the injured party," Proroc said.

"Where is the goat? Can it stand on its three legs?" Anton asked.

"Yes, Anton, it could if it were a dog. You know how dogs hop about on three legs, but a goat, the most stupid creature in the world, wants four legs or it won't walk," Proroc said.

"Then I will have to carry her, you mean?" Anton said and spat disgustedly.

"Well, Anton, that is why I asked Gherasim to come. It is an old goat. One leg broken. Actually, it is a maimed animal, not much use. He could judge for himself. Maybe it would only pay for the damage it did," Proroc said.

Anton had been with Uncle Gherasim many years. He had learned much and was nobody's fool. He said, "All would be well but for one thing, Proroc. You cannot prove that it was not your intention to maim the goat. Now, because you cannot prove that, you are guilty and the goat is innocent. And something else. It is innocent and injured besides. Injured by you. There you have the whole matter as plain as the wart on your nose. It is you who must pay damages to Uncle Gherasim. But as everybody knows, he is a good man. He will let you pay for the goat only, and forget the kid."

Proroc stared at Anton. He was angry and scared too. But he must not lose his head. He started to smile and then he laughed and said, "Like master, like servant. Ho ho, Anton, you have a good tongue. Yes, indeed. And what kid do you mean, Anton?"

"The goat is going to kid, Proroc," Anton said. "So, you pay Uncle Gherasim for the injury to the goat alone and leave the kid to its fate."

The affair remained unsettled because Proroc wanted to have Uncle Gherasim come to him. That would give him the satisfaction of telling everybody, "Gherasim came to me about the damage caused me by his goat." Besides, if he paid for the goat, as Anton threatened he would have to, it would be much easier for him to bargain at his own home—a man is supreme master in his house—and so he would have the kid in payment for the damage, which after all was really slight. As to the goat, he had figured that if its leg got mended he would keep it for breeding; if, however, it became necessary to slaughter it, he should do it on a Saturday when most housewives would be glad to buy a piece of meat for Sunday. He could draw profit out of that also.

Anton told Uncle Gherasim what Proroc wanted, and that the goat had a broken leg. "Proroc broke it, he admitted," Anton said.

"I will go," Uncle Gherasim said.

"Shall I come along? In case the goat has to be carried," Anton said.

"No, you stay at home. If the goat cannot walk, Proroc will carry it," Uncle Gherasim said, and went.

"Welcome, Gherasim, come in the house," Proroc said at the gate.

147

"Thank you, but I have no time. Where is my prize goat? Anton tells me you broke its leg," Uncle Gherasim said. "Such an animal. I can't replace it. Where is the poor creature?"

"How do you mean, Gherasim, 'prize animal'? I have eyes. It is a goat like any goat," Proroc said.

"We have eyes, yet we see only what we know. Where is the goat, Proroc?" Uncle Gherasim said.

"It is under the shed. Lying on clean straw. We took care of the broken leg," Proroc said. He led Uncle Gherasim to the shed.

The goat was chewing the cud, its lower jaw shuttling from side to side, and looked up as the men entered the shed. It did not try to get up on its feet.

"She is crippled, I see. Now show me your damage," Uncle Gherasim said.

They went in the orchard. Proroc pointed out several trees where—he said—the goat had broken off the ends of some branches.

"Very well, Proroc. I have both sides of the matter now. This is your damage. Mine is the maimed goat. We can settle the affair easily. I pay you for your damage, you pay me for mine. How much do you want, Proroc?" Uncle Gherasim said.

"It is an old creature, this goat of yours, and . . ." Proroc started saying, but Uncle Gherasim cut him short. "Leave the goat out. Tell me how much you want for the damage."

"Well, you can judge for yourself. The price of the goat would cover the damage," Proroc said.

"Very good. And what price would you set on the old, maimed creature? You said it is old and maimed," Uncle Gherasim said.

148

Proroc was in a trap. He realized it. He said, "Of course, Gherasim, I have my way of judging, you have yours. You said it is a prize goat, I said an old goat, so how can we set the price on it? We must agree somehow. So, I say, let us set the price midway, between a prize goat and an old goat."

"Very well, that would be about fifty kronen," Uncle Gherasim said.

"Yes, about fifty kronen, I agree," Proroc said.

"Now the damage to my goat, we must settle that," Uncle Gherasim said.

"How is that, Gherasim?" Proroc asked, amazed.

"Do not play the fool, Proroc. You suffered a damage, and I make good to you for it. I suffered a damage and you must make good to me," Uncle Gherasim said.

"But the goat, Gherasim. You set the price at fifty kronen, the damage to me is fifty kronen; so, one covers the other. I keep the goat and we part good friends," Proroc said.

No, he was all wrong. He saw only his side, Uncle Gherasim told him. There were two damages to be settled, not one, and if Uncle Gherasim made good, Proroc had to make good too. It was not easy to have him see the light as Uncle Gherasim held it up to him, but at long last Proroc gave up the haggling. His damage was fifty kronen, and so was Uncle Gherasim's. One damage canceled the other. And Proroc had to carry the lame goat to Uncle Gherasim's. But he had the satisfaction that Uncle Gherasim came to him, admitted that his goat had caused him damage, and made good for it. And from that time on, the whole village knew how many days Proroc gained on Uncle Gherasim each year.

CHAPTER 17

൦൦൦൦൦൦൦൦൦൦൦൦

UNCLE GHERASIM SAID THAT THE POOREST MAN IS NOT the one who has nothing but the miser who has and cannot enjoy what he has in a natural way. "The miser is not a whole person," he used to say.

When mother asked him what was the natural way he said, "The natural way for healthy men and women is to eat well, drink a little too, exchange gifts, live in good, clean homes, raise families, and when they need buy something for their pleasure, buy it without counting the money paid for it more than twice."

He said that those who count their money more than twice forfeit half of the pleasure they could derive from a purchase.

Father observed that he—Uncle Gherasim—was master at driving a bargain.

"Well, I shall not deny it, I do like to bargain and am not too bad at it," Uncle Gherasim said, "but I always buy what I want to have, and I never count the price more than twice." He laughed.

150

Father glanced at mother, with his left eyebrow up, and mother blushed. This time he scored against her without saying a word.

In our family mother managed all the buying for the household, and she actually reckoned more than twice, more than three times, what she had and what she could spend, *for the most needed things.* It was a serious and taxing business for her. She would sit at the table and quietly enumerate what had to be provided. Then she would look at one of us—we never disturbed her at such moments—look earnestly, as if a solution might be revealed to her from such gazing.

Father could never bear this for more than a few minutes. He would quietly leave the table and the room. We could not say whether mother missed him or even noticed when he was leaving. She seemed in a trance, so concentrated she was.

If father told her that she took it too seriously, that she could not increase the amount of money she had, no matter how concentrated her gaze at one of us, mother would answer that one member of the family had to take serious matters seriously.

"But, Barbara dear, it does not help anyway," father would say.

"I cannot understand you, dear. You are so intelligent, but sometimes you amaze me. How can you say it does not help?" mother would say.

"Well, Barbara, think a little. Does it help really? Does it make the amount of money you have double itself?" father would say.

"It is really a pity, dear, with a mind like yours, that you would not think a little yourself. The money need not double itself if your purchase can be doubled," mother would say.

"And how can the purchase double itself, Barbara dear? Tell me, I am willing to think," father would say.

Mother contended that if he really was willing to think he could see that she was right and, if she was going to tell him everything then he need not bother his head with thinking. Yet, she would tell him this much: "If you know how much hardship the earning of money entails, you will do everything to make it go twice as far as the money of those to whom it comes easily."

Father could take this to mean concern about his work, or as a reminder that practicing law in a large city would be more lucrative, and so with a richer budget, mother's task of managing the household would be much easier too.

Whichever way he took it, these remained the last words in the discussion, and they were mother's.

I do not believe that father ever realized mother's difficulties. It seemed most natural to him that mother should manage as she did because he brought to her practically every penny he earned. And if sometimes he had very little to give and still no pinch was felt in the house, he did not ask how it was possible to be so. Actually, mother was a mother to him too, not only to Irina and me. He felt the same security in the home as we children felt. And mother never disappointed him. Because of this, he would tell her not to take so seriously the business of expenditures, as if, in his opinion, she could accomplish her task easily by the mere fact that it was *her* task. A mother can fulfill her mission under any circumstances—believes the child.

I remember when we would have no meat for dinner. There would be vegetable soup, purée of beans or lentils, and plum jam or such meatless dishes.

Father would have the soup and the rest and then, before taking the jam, he would be all smiles and say to mother, "Barbara dear, is there no meat of any kind in your house?"

"But it is Friday, dear, we do not take meat on Fridays," mother would say.

"I know, Barbara, but I feel so hungry for a little piece of meat. A small piece of ham or beef," father would say, his eyes bright with confidence that mother could produce what he desired. She always did.

Of course this would not happen every Friday, but when it did happen, father had his wish. Mother used to say that father was as bad as a pregnant woman when he desired something.

Actually we should have observed two meatless days throughout the year, not mentioning Lent before Christmas and Easter when all days were meatless, but father said if we kept one day rigorously we did well, for actually had not Christ said, "It is no sin what you put in your mouth but what comes out of it." He always repeated these words when mother warned him of sinning if he ate meat on forbidden days.

The truth is that father was more spoiled than we children were. He was past master at wheedling. Sometimes, after mother would give in to him, she would suddenly turn and say, "And I do not believe half of your flattery. No!" To which father would invariably answer, "Barbara dear, that is good. If you believe half of the truth I am telling, the other half follows by its own nature."

Mother had great admiration for learned persons and she considered father a very learned man. But she was not blind to his weaknesses, and if she overlooked them it was because of her love for him. Perhaps what she considered to be the greatest lack in his character was ambition. And, were she not so deeply religious, she would certainly have goaded him more strongly and kept after him until he took a decisive step that would prove either that his ambition was higher than mere worldly success or that he needed just such goading. But father was happy with his state, and who dares take away the happiness of the loved one with the sole justification of reason born of convention?

Mother knew very well that striving after earthly riches was less commendable than seeking spiritual riches. Therefore, she reduced her complaints correspondingly. Then too, she was a very good manager, and while saying she did not believe father's flattery she always blushed with pleasure hearing it.

Mother did not want riches but she wished she could be freer with money. When she made her budget, counting the money for the several needed items, setting each amount separately, there was such an expression of sweet sadness in her face and posture that we children watched her spellbound, as if she were on the point of performing some miracle. She did not count aloud but moved her lips as when praying, which made her attitude still more impressive to us. And then she would take a few coins from one counted amount and add them to another, or, deducting a little from each, make a new amount, and then give a sigh of relief and lift her eyes to look at the

154

Virgin Mary on the icon. And then she would smile. Perhaps she did accomplish some miracle. If she did she was giving her thanks to the image on the icon.

Mother believed that we must always be thankful for the least favor because by doing so, we demonstrate that we deserve more. I wondered later why mother did not receive more and greater favors from heaven, because she never omitted her thanks for the least she received.

Father's relation with the heavenly powers was neither so intimate nor so humble as mother's. He had reverence, and when he asked the blessing of our food at table there came an expression of piety in his face, which was as convincing as his frown when angry. But then, he was a man and he prayed to a masculine God, and an attitude of man to man does not require either cajolery or supplication. "Father, you know my burden. I have a family. You provided us this food for this meal. Thank you, Amen." This, in a nutshell, would be father's prayer.

After all, God made us, so there is parental responsibility resting on His shoulders too. And a man is what he is and father was a soldierly man. He walked with his chest out, head high, and swung his heavy cane like a band leader. He called me little soldier, made wooden swords, and taught me a few fencing movements. "Always look your opponent in the eye," he cautioned me.

But I did not like to be a soldier. I wanted to be a Haiduk like Bujor or Radu Negru who were very brave. They feared nobody. And they took from the rich and gave to the poor. They were the friends of the people. They even defied the gendarmes and the soldiers. They were as clever as they were fearless. And I had seen

155

soldiers but never had I seen a Haiduk, therefore I could invest the Haiduk in fancy with all the marvelous qualities of the heroes in Uncle Gherasim's tales.

Sometimes I wished father were a Haiduk. Then he would take me on his exploits and make me a Haiduk too. I admired him greatly and he could not help being so very commanding, having been an officer in the army. Mother had told us how handsome he had looked in uniform.

Then too, since the home is a man's kingdom and the king is the highest ranking officer, father's commanding attitude was his right. He might have been an out-and-out tyrant because kings can be tyrants, yet he was only soldierly strict. That was discipline, and discipline is the highest of man's achievements, he said. Nothing of real worth can be accomplished without discipline. He said that religion and everything beautiful, like music, poetry, painting, sculpture, architecture, the dance, were forms of discipline and the results of it. Without discipline man would be an animal, he said.

Father played the flute quite well, but he was a much better drummer. On national holidays when all the men formed into rank and paraded from one end of the village to the other, since they had no band they sang, and after the singing had stopped, father kept up the martial spirit by beating the drum. And how proudly he marched at the head of the column, his head high, for he was indeed no ordinary drummer. The men who had their military service said he was one in a thousand. Discipline, evidently, discipline of the hands. And thanks to father's great belief in discipline, he decided to teach us dancing.

He started with the quadrille because it implied grace

156

of movement and no intricate steps. We had no music at first so father merely clapped his hands for the tempo and whistled something that sounded like a march, and gave his command too. Of course he executed each figure first, by himself, and it was amusing to see him obey his own orders. I laughed but mother frowned at me and I covered my mouth.

Later father taught Nicodin the tune. It was pleasant to hear it played on the shepherd fife—if only our dancing master had been Uncle Gherasim instead of father.

Uncle Gherasim seemed to have all the time in the world to explain something while father had only so much time for one thing, and if you did not grasp his instruction in that period of time, you were left for a dullard. That is what happened to me in the quadrille. After having collided twice with Irina and once with father, I was told to stay out and watch the others. On that evening Uncle Gherasim came. The instruction was still going on.

Skirting the dancers Uncle Gherasim found me sitting alone near the table which was pushed to the far end of the room. "You are resting, Peter," he said and sat down by me. Father was facing us at that moment. When his back was turned I whispered to Uncle Gherasim, "I am being punished. I have failed at that dancing."

Uncle Gherasim bent to my ear and whispered, "You have not failed, Peter, you only did not give yourself enough time to learn it," and he patted me on the head. Then he straightened up and assumed a serious mien. Father had turned to face us once more. Mother smiled at us.

While watching the dance and having me do likewise

so as not to disobey father, Uncle Gherasim spoke to me barely loud enough to be heard. "You see, Peter," he said, "we can learn practically anything we want to, but the time one person or another needs differs in length. And once you have learned what you have taken up, who will ask how much time you gave to it? The important thing is your wanting to learn."

I felt very happy because Uncle Gherasim spoke to me taking it for granted—or perhaps he merely wished me to feel happy—that I understood him. One thing, however, is true, that what Uncle Gherasim told me I never forgot, though I did forget much of what teacher Vlad gave us as instruction. Uncle Gherasim never said, "I will teach you so and so," but, "This is how we do it; this is how we know it; this is how you can do it." It always came to how I could do something actually, with never a doubt about it. Any teaching or advice from Uncle Gherasim had the quality of a gift.

He had an astounding memory for fact and also a visual memory. He told me once, "Our saying, 'To steal with the eyes,' is not mere words; it tells a plain truth." And when he showed me a plant or a bug I had not seen before, his advice was, "Look at it well, Peter, so as to have it imprinted on your mind. Steal with your eyes."

As we were watching father demonstrate the figures of the quadrille, Uncle Gherasim said to me quietly, "Remember, Peter, what I told you, steal with your eyes." I did.

I remember to this day how father moved, and every one of his postures, but I never became a dancer. He taught us the waltz and the polka and two Romanian folk dances, the sirba and the reel. My eyes were excellent thieves, but my feet preferred ordinary walking and running.

I believe father realized this and since he was a perfectionist and had high regard for the dance, he did not insist on making a dancer of me.

᭣᭣᭣᭣᭣᭣᭣᭣᭣᭣᭣᭣

CHAPTER 18

ALL THE SEASONS WERE LONG FOR US CHILDREN.
When in the beginning of winter father would say, "Next
spring I shall plant twice as many tomatoes as this year,"
spring seemed to me terribly far away. As to a whole year,
that was a long stretch of time indeed.

Of all the seasons winter was the longest. Actually too,
not merely because the summer seemed shorter, since after
the two months' vacation from school it was already over
for me. Winter set in in the early days of November, with
the first snow, and stayed with us until March. And when
the warm days came and the snow began to melt, there
was the very first snow too, under layers of others that fell
during the winter. I wondered in those days which snow
melted first, the topmost layer or the nethermost. When I
asked Nicodin, he said, "It seems to me, Peter, now that
you made me give it a thought, the first snow will melt
first. Not that it will start first to melt. No! The last snow,
which is on top, will start melting first, but the heat of the
sun will penetrate down to the very earth and the earth
will hold the warmth, being so thickly covered with snow,

160

even after the sun sets. It is like when you go out in the sun in a heavy coat. After a while your body will sweat and will continue to sweat for some time even if you should go in the cool cellar. Well, Peter, the body of the earth sweats too, and so, the snow that fell first will go first."

When Nicodin was asked a question, he always pondered before he answered. To a difficult question like this about the snow, he invariably introduced his answer with "It seems to me . . ." But on simple matters he was direct and positive, concluding with "It is as I say."

And when a thing was "as he said," the bishop himself could not gainsay Nicodin's affirmation. To mother, however, he made allowance, not grudgingly, but with such an expression of kind indulgence that mother would give the subject a second thought. He was uncanny about telling the hour at any time of the day, even if it was cloudy, although he was more accurate on sunny days.

For me it was not the clock that measured time, but my activities; therefore, I admired Nicodin who could serve as a living timepiece. I believed that he could tell the hour because, always doing something, he knew by what he had accomplished how much time the work had "eaten up."

It was Nicodin's way of putting it. When father gave him a job to do, he would think a few moments, then say, "Very good, I shall do it. It will eat up half of the day."

Naturally, every kind of work ate up time and squeezed the sweat out of the peasant's brow as the Lord had ordained. The folk had no complaint against it, but what irked them terribly was when the waiting at the communal house for a piece of legal paper ate up their valuable time.

161

And few were the transactions a peasant could make without a paper permit from the authorities.

On market day the peasants crowded into the *cancelarie*, the office of the mayor and notary, to obtain what were called Sales Certificates. These were papers that gave a man the right and the permission to sell a sheep, goat, pig, cow, horse, ox, colt, and of course each paper bore fiscal stamps which the man paid for besides the fee for clerical work.

One could sell fowls of every kind without such papers, but none of the four-legged animals. It was simple enough why. Nobody would buy such an animal without the proper certificate, which bore witness that the named animal was the rightful property of the vendor. And the buyer must have the certificate, once more legalized at this transaction, with more fiscal stamps added to it and another clerical fee, else he could not resell the merchandise or prove that it actually belonged to him.

But how does the original owner of a cow prove that the animal is his in case he raised it himself from a calf of one of his cows? That again was simple. The calf was registered at the *cancelarie* when it was born. Every head of cattle, sheep, and other animals owned by the inhabitants of a village were registered in special, huge registers, and this was also the notary's work.

The peasants said it was all done so the government could extract more money from the poor people and to make it easy for the tax collector to put a lien on a man's animals and actually take them for nonpayment of taxes on a fixed date.

Of course the man could redeem his confiscated property in a given period of time and pay the delinquency charge besides the tax, else it was sold at auction. But the tax collector also had to have the certificate of ownership from the man whose chattel he confiscated.

I had been home two days for my summer vacation when, in the early morning, I heard Nicodin speaking loudly to someone who was asking for father. I ran out. In the yard were a very tall Saxon and a buffalo cow. He was holding the end of the rope by which the animal was tied.

It turned out that we were receiving the buffalo cow in payment for legal work father had done for Hans Rigger, the Saxon. Father was pleased and mother too, for the milk of buffalo cows is very rich. But poor Hans Rigger discovered after emptying his belt pocket of all its contents that he had forgotten the certificate of ownership at home. Of course nobody would suspect a man like Hans Rigger of theft, but he felt mortified. We should please believe him, he raised the cow on his farm and had the necessary document to prove it. He would bring it to us on the coming Sunday, if father would please wait, because there was so much work at home and even his daughter could not be spared. He took four hours getting to us, but, having bought a horse from our miller, he would ride home in less than an hour, he said. And they really needed the horse very much at this season, he added. Because they needed the horse and Rigger had to come for it, he had brought the buffalo that day.

Father reassured the man. "Nobody will question us about the buffalo between Tuesday and Sunday," he said, but Rigger must not forget to have the certificate brought

163

to us. "We shall give the cow over to the village cowherd," father explained, "and in case it strays away we must be able to claim it when found."

Hans Rigger saw the whole affair clearly, he said, and once more expressed his regrets for causing us this inconvenience. He was in too great a hurry to come in the house for a little refreshment, so mother brought out plum brandy, black olives, and bread, of which the three men, father, Rigger, and Nicodin, were served by mother. She herself merely touched the glass to her lips for politeness.

I learned then what a serious affair it was to own cattle. Not even as a gift could you have any without a proper legal document.

The European buffalo is a strange animal indeed. To believe it, it must be seen. To begin with, it is coal black, and has very thick, ridged horns, twisted like the horns of a ram. And then its nature. Nicodin, who was very clever with animals, got to understand it quickly enough, but Luca, the cowherd, had trouble. The buffalo has a will and a stubbornness equal to the proverbial stubbornness of the mule, and is terribly slow-witted to boot. And then, on warm days, it cannot resist anything that promises a cooling, be it a muddy pool, brook, or river.

That is what Luca found out about our buffalo cow the first day he had it in the herd. To reach the communal pastures, Luca drove his herd by the marshes where the villagers thaw and cure the hemp. All went as usual with the herd, our buffalo shambling along with the rest of the cows until they came to the marshes. There, as Luca told us, "The black devil broke out from the herd and made for the mire. I ran to stop her, but the creature bore down on me as if I were not a human being but a corn stalk that it could trample down. I will say I used my whip. The beast must have thought I was lashing at the flies on its thick head. It got into the mud and laid itself down. Then it raised its ugly head and looked at me. I spat and crossed myself, for the beast looked like Satan himself staring at me."

We had to recognize Luca's difficulties. Father promised him a pair of new boots for Christmas, which Luca received in due time, with many thanks and great joy. After he had the promise of a pair of boots Luca never complained to us about the buffalo, and when he actually received them, he said the creature could not help being what it was. "There are enough stubborn and stupid people too," he said, "and God alone knows why."

During that summer mother fed me about a quart of buffalo milk daily. It is very good, and nearly as rich as ewe's milk. My sister found it too rich for her and mother did not insist, but let her have cow's milk.

But now we had so much of this staple food that every day mother gave five or six quarts to neighbors who had growing children and not enough milk from their one cow or goat. We also had butter and pot cheese in plenty, of which some of the poorer people received a share.

Father was a great meat eater. He preferred meat to all other food, and wanted to have it daily. But mother had now so much of the dairy products that she prepared all sorts of dishes with cheese, sour cream, sour milk, such as sour milk dumplings, cheese pie or cake, mushrooms with

165

sour cream, balmesh (cornmeal cooked in cream), and many other real delicacies, as she called them. Everyone in our home relished this food, but not father.

"No, Barbara. I am not an invalid and I am not a growing child. I need meat. That is food for me," father protested.

"I know, dear, you like meat and are used to it too, so you cannot all at once taste the full flavor and delicacy of these wonderful dishes. Naturally you have to give yourself a little time, and then you will relish them more than meat. Yes, dear, more than meat," mother said.

"A little more time you say, Barbara? A hundred years is a little time to you?" father said.

"How could I mean a hundred years, dear? We do not live so long," mother said earnestly. Sometimes she really overplayed the naïveté, which made the veins on father's temple swell and thump.

"Good Lord! Good Holy Father! Please, Barbara," father shouted, "Please, just please keep quiet. I want meat, meat, and—ah!" he was too angry to say more. He ran to the door, jumped back, snatched his hat from the peg, jammed it on his head, and rushed out.

Mother sighed as she looked through the window to see father on the street. She was sad, but suddenly she sat down and covered her face. She did not weep. She started to laugh, at first quietly, then with all her rippling laughter. She sat there and laughed, her face covered with her hands.

It is true, there was something very comical about father when he got angry, especially when it was mother who aroused his temper. It appeared that he had no defense against what he called her "naïveté." And so he re-

166

mained puzzled for a short moment while his ire was making ready to flame up. That was the moment that inspired laughter, for he looked, in that short time, lost and helpless.

I remember one time when mother told him that Rafila, a woman who occasionally did work for us, said she would die at the end of four years. Rafila was sixty years old, but she looked well and could work, too, without complaining of fatigue.

"How does she know? She looks like one who would live to be eighty," father said.

"Yes, dear. I told her so, but she said, 'You will see, you will see. I know it absolutely. There is only enough life in me to last four more years. I am all used up.' Is not this stoicism wonderful, dear? Rafila never slows up, she works as hard as ever, and there at the end of four years she sees the grave waiting for her," mother said.

"Barbara dear, that is all stupid nonsense, not stoicism. She does not know how long she is going to live and she does not see the grave waiting for her," father said.

"But she is all used up, dear. She knows that," mother said.

"No! I say she does not know how far she is used up. At any rate it is just idiocy. What have we to bother about it?" father said.

"That is why I told you, dear," mother said gently. "I wish you would speak to her. She may be right, but you can cheer her up, dear, you speak so wonderfully."

That puzzled look came into father's eyes. He got red. The veins on his temple thumped. Then he snapped, "I will tell her to go to the devil now, not in four years."

"God forgive you, dear," mother said quietly and

lowered her head because father was staring at her now. The next moment he turned on his heels and very deliberately walked out.

Mother raised her eyes, looked at the door, and then she smiled and covered her face.

⊙⊙⊙⊙⊙⊙⊙⊙⊙⊙⊙⊙⊙

CHAPTER 19

JUST AS FATHER WAS A GREAT MEAT EATER, SO mother was a great lover of coffee. Not that she drank more than two cups of it daily, but she could not do without it. Breakfast and four o'clock without coffee would have been a misfortune. Mother took her coffee with boiled milk and when we got the buffalo cow, the milk from this animal—so much richer than cow's milk—made the coffee even more delicious for mother.

If friends from the city praised the coffee mother served them, she would tell them with a bit of pride that it was the buffalo milk that gave it the fine taste.

Irina and I had our milk merely sprinkled with a few drops of the precious brew, but we said we were having coffee. And, too, we drank our allotted daily portion of milk with more pleasure because of the few drops of coffee. Not that we found any difference in the taste of the milk, but because it had an infinitesimal quantity of what to mother was the elixir of life.

Our buffalo cow was indeed a great asset in our household economy. This was not merely because of the milk she furnished us, but because mother found that we children liked this milk better than goat's milk, and so we made a good meal of it once a day in the variety of preparations mother was skillful at. We did relish the sour cream or sour milk and corn bread, but much more the sour-cream dumplings doused with molten butter and noodles cooked in milk.

When we got the buffalo cow, mother firmly believed that she would win father over to reduce his meat diet at least by a quarter, by two days a week, for example, when she would prepare some delicious milk dishes for him. Of course she failed.

Did he not like the sour-cream dumplings, she asked? Certainly he did, father said, as a side dish. And how about noodles cooked in milk? Very good, father said, but not more than a few spoonfuls now and then after his daily siesta. And mushrooms in sour milk? Yes, very good for an appetizer, once a week. And rice pudding with sugar and cinnamon? Good dessert, father admitted, but he preferred goat cheese. Wine tasted better after cheese than after rice pudding.

Then she asked father if he did not notice how much better we all looked, mother and we children, since we were eating less meat and more milk and the milk products. Yes, indeed, he had noticed that, and had mother noticed that he himself was perhaps less robust, less energetic, and less capable of work than formerly?

God forbid, no, she saw no such signs. "Well then, you and the children thrive on the buffalo cow's milk, with God's and my blessing, and I will keep to the eating of meat," father said.

It was in the year when we received the buffalo cow that a young woman told my fortune, using no other means to divine the future than a certain number of beans. White beans. Mother did not believe in any form of forecasting. She believed that the future was in the hands of God, and the human being could not and was not meant to know it. Therefore, when she had the women at our house, she never had them indulge in fortunetelling.

Several women in our village "had the gift," it was said. We knew them well. Of course they practiced also incantations, especially against the evil eye, and were supposed to know something of sorcery and witchcraft. But since both sorcery and witchcraft are, in the belief of the people, tinged with the working of Satan, the women disclaimed any practice of such.

Still, in extreme cases, when the devil, by some tricks of his own, got hold of a mortal, man or woman, and exorcism was not or did not prove quite helpful, a trial by darker means than just incantation was permissible. This was not sorcery or witchcraft, but some practice that could outwit the devil himself.

Of such things much was rumored and nothing actually proven. So the women who had knowledge of soothsaying and the gift of scanning the future contented themselves with these.

Girls of marriageable age had one short period of time in each year when they could ask what the future held for them and be answered. But their question was very simple indeed. All they wanted to know was if they would marry that year and have a glimpse of the man.

The time for such practice was the hour of twelve, when the old year expires and the new year is born.

171

The girl must be either alone or only with other girls in her position. That is, in quest of a revelation of the future, and as naked as she was born. She must prepare a piece of lead, about the size of a small walnut, and have it molten, so that when the hour strikes twelve, she can pour it into cold water, where the lead will take prophetic form.

When several girls are together they can, if they so choose, show one another what each obtained. Naturally there would be one among them who could see more in the cryptic shape the lead took when dropped in the water, and so she could tell the others what her own fancy revealed to herself.

Elisaveta Corbu, the young woman who looked into my future, had been several years earlier one of the girls among six who could tell each one of them more than they could see in the lead.

The story went that her own symbol looked like a large dog on top of a rock, beneath and leaning against which was something that could be the figure of a man, unless it was a small fir tree.

Elisaveta had no difficulty interpreting the forecast. The dog meant watch. The rock on which it stood was a mountain. The small figure was a man. A shepherd. The man destiny chose for her was a shepherd.

At the time Elisaveta was reading her own future from the cryptic symbol cast in lead by the hand of chance, Mihail Corbu, her sweetheart, was in the army. He was not a shepherd. Until he was taken into the army he helped his widowed mother at working their land, which was barely enough to keep them and the smaller brothers and sisters of Mihail alive. There were two girls and two boys besides Mihail.

Elisaveta was saddened by the prophecy, for she loved Mihail and he loved her. And she could not read the forecast in any other way. Her own parents had a few sheep, and she being the only daughter (her two brothers were married already), she might have the sheep as part of her dowry, but they were not enough to warrant Mihail giving his time to herd them.

That year Mihail came home. He had finished his military service. "We shall get married when the grapes are pressed this autumn," he said to Elisaveta.

"I love you, Mihail, with all my heart, but . . ." She did not say what was on her mind.

Mihail pressed to know. What did she mean with her but? Had she, perhaps, been promised by her parents to another man?

No! Nothing like that really. And to all his importunate questioning Elisaveta's best answer was that he should have patience. Time would answer for Elisaveta. "The Lord grant it shall be as my heart craves," she said.

Then, in the month of May, Elisaveta said, the fortunate thing happened. Popa Radu came to Uncle Gherasim. He wanted a reliable young man to herd his brother's sheep. Uncle Gherasim recommended Mihail and he was hired. One of his brothers was now old enough to take his place.

"So, you see, I did marry a shepherd and the choice of my heart," Lisaveta said. She was a lovely young woman. Father always pinched her chin when she came to us, which was only a few times a year because she lived with Mihail in another village during the winter, and in the summer went with him and the sheep to the mountains.

I had my future told in a cabin about one day's travel by horse from our village. I was by then a veteran moun-

173

taineer and mother was not concerned about my riding with Uncle Gherasim and four young women who were going to pick wild raspberries on the mountain slopes.

We put up at Lisaveta's for the first night. There I met Nutza, the mother of John the "Village Saint," whose story I wrote many years later, and which caused my book of collected tales to be banned in America for a period of two years.

Elisaveta welcomed us with open arms, actually, saying she had had a presentiment that friends would come. She kissed me and held me close to her and said I had grown since last she saw me. Uncle Gherasim said it might be the buffalo milk, and everybody laughed. Mihail had gone for provisions and would not be home until the next morning. The sheep were in the pen, the two dogs inside the fence, at the gate, lying on the ground with muzzles right under the gate. They made no sound at our approach. Uncle Gherasim said their noses told them we were friends. "Lisaveta has presentiments but all that her dogs have is a good nose," he said.

We all had our own food but Elisaveta contributed the spring water, which was of the best in the world, Uncle Gherasim said, and her great cheerfulness.

Then, after we had our supper, the women asked to have their fortunes told. Elisaveta needed no coaxing. She brought the beans at once. Then she said, "First I will cast the beans for Peter. He, being the youngest, has a longer future than all of us." She counted out the required number, formed them into a heap which she patted three times, and three times turned them round under a hand cupped over them, while she murmured some words we could not hear. Then she asked me to make the sign of the cross over the pile, after which again she repeated some words and divided the beans in three uneven piles as chance or the spirit of divination led her hand.

The women were bending over the table, all attention and curiosity, but Uncle Gherasim smoked his pipe leaning back against the wall, his eyes on me. Several times I glanced up at him, for I felt his gaze. He answered my glances with a lift of his bushy eyebrows.

Elisaveta looked for a long time at the three piles of beans, then she touched the one on the left and said, "Before you have grown into a man you will travel far, far, over countries and seas. Good fortune will be on your side. And here," she said, touching the second pile, "I see that before you leave our land you shall go away from your home and have longing alone for it but no sight of it. And here," her fingers touched the third pile, "you are told of sadness. It will come into your heart while you are still of tender age."

"Ileana will get married. But do not cry over it, Peter, she is too old for you," Uncle Gherasim teased me, chuckling. I blushed. The young women laughed but Elisaveta came and took me in her arms and kissed me.

The sadness she forecast came only too soon. And, strangely, the rest of her prediction came true also. Could I have ever dreamed that I would leave my native land, and the home in the village that I loved so dearly? And yet, such was the will of my fates.

What was Elisaveta's great oracular gift that revealed to her so much in the humble beans? For I avow, in all sincerity and truth, that what she told me has come to pass.

175

At the time, of course, I took it all as any child of my age would, but with the child's freshness of memory, I absorbed every word of Elisaveta's to remember until my last breath.

But in the immediate future I did not recall her predictions. It remained imprinted in my mind to rise to the surface when her prophecies started to come true.

In the mountains Uncle Gherasim took me in hand once more "to make a man of me," as he said. The first two days he allowed me to go in the afternoon with the berry pickers. That was enchanting. The women sang and chatted and laughed while their hands worked with amazing rapidity.

On the second afternoon we were in a dense patch of raspberry bushes. Two of the women, who were about a hundred yards from us, fell suddenly silent. They had been singing before, while my group had been listening. "Ho, Raveca, what struck you dumb?" one of the women called.

No answer from Raveca. Instead, we heard a great sucking noise and the crackling of broken twigs. The noise was approaching us. Then we saw the bear. He was harvesting the raspberry in his own way, sucking the clusters off the bush and slowly moving forward. The creature raised its head once or twice to look at us and moved it as if nodding and that was all. He passed by us within thirty paces. In a short time the two women joined us and the group remained together.

"The beast came straight at us. We did not hear it until there it was. I got so frightened something happened to me. And don't laugh," Raveca said. She had her apron

176

and skirt tucked up into her belt. Her legs were bare to above her knees.

"We were not afraid, we had a man with us," one woman said as she patted me on the head.

We told Uncle Gherasim what had happened. He said the bear will not touch human beings in the summer when there are berries and wild honey. "The bear prefers this food to human flesh. But he is dangerous when he comes out of his winter sleep, lean and famished," he said.

On our way home we stopped again at Elisaveta's. When we left she told me to remember her when I would be far away. I had no inkling what she was referring to and thought she meant that the city where I went to school was so far, far away.

During that summer mother complained more often of headaches but she looked well and on good days was as cheerful as ever. She attributed her otherwise good health to the milk from the buffalo cow and the wholesome cottage cheese.

Father suggested, of course, that this milk should cure her headaches too, since it had such wonderful virtues, but mother said that the cure of a malady which she had had so many years was in the hands of God.

The last few days of August, before I returned to school in the city, were very happy at home. Mother was preparing things for me to take along. She often sang quietly, sitting at her sewing table on the porch, her feet on a footstool. Her voice had the quality that I had associated with the closing of a summer day, the time when the sun is just setting and the long shadows of trees and buildings bring the first coolness of the evening to come. It was sweet and fresh with a tinge of sadness in it, not of deep-rooted sorrow like the voice of Floare, the woman who lost her husband and the two sons at "one stroke of fate," but that sweet little sorrow which I felt at the end of a beautiful day because it was gone and the thought of the coming day was not yet born in my mind.

Mother cooked rice pudding for me nearly every day and sprinkled the creamy delicacy with cinnamon mixed with powdered sugar. On the last day before my departure she baked a great number of milk-and-butter rolls, the dough leavened with yeast, rolls that were as tasty when a week old as when fresh. My school friends in the city had known these rolls since my first year and now, each time I returned from a vacation at home, they expected me to bring some.

Irina remained at home. She had completed her schooling in the city and was growing into a woman, our neighbors said. It is true she was tall for her age, and young men followed her with their eyes when she walked in the street. Everybody said she was beautiful but myself, who, at the time, had only eyes for such loveliness as was Ileana's, the daughter of one-eyed John, and for Mena who was only Irina's age.

As usual, mother had tears in her eyes although she smiled when she bade me farewell and I climbed into the carriage where father had already taken his place.

Irina had kissed me on the forehead, very patronizingly, as if such a kiss from her was a priceless gift for me but a mere trifle for the giver.

It was very early in the morning. The sun was rising from behind the hill. Uncle Gherasim knew this was the

178

hour of leaving. When we came up to his house he was at the gate, a small, new wooden pail in his hand. From under the rim of the cover protruded a fringe of green.

Nicodin drew up and stopped the horses. "So, you are on your way, Peter," Uncle Gherasim said after we exchanged greetings. *It is honey in that bucket, covered with grape leaves under the wooden cover,* I was thinking. "I know you will not give cause of displeasure to your good parents. You will put that bright head of yours to work. That is good, Peter," Uncle Gherasim said. He made no move to offer me the bucket. *Perhaps it is a gift for mother,* I thought, a bit regretfully, because if it was for her he should have brought it earlier and then she would have given me some of it to take along.

Uncle Gherasim asked father to be so good as to attend to some legal work of which they had spoken before. Father said he would, he had enough time in the city on this trip. He asked a few questions which Uncle Gherasim answered deliberately. He seemed to have forgotten the bucket altogether as he held it at his side. Then father said, "Good health to you, Uncle Gherasim, we are departing."

"The Lord conduct you safely," Uncle Gherasim said. And then, as Nicodin was on the point of starting the horses, he said, "I have a little gift for you, Peter," and reached the bucket to me. It was honey. Golden honey, in the comb, which my friends at Mrs. Bart's and Lina the servant girl and myself ate, comb and all. The wax of the comb was nearly as fragrant as the honey itself. One of the boys who had pilfered some of the honey in my absence and had asked another portion besides what I had given him got a little sick. Lina said nobody would get

179

sick from honey and to blame a bellyache on honey was a sin. "I could eat half a bucketful if somebody gave it to me," she said. I believed her. Lina was as strong as a man. When she did the laundry, she lifted a huge basketful of the wet clothes and carried it down a steep flight of stairs into the yard to hang and dry. And at one time when Nicodin said he would kiss her she said simply, "Try it." He tried and she held him off.

"This female creature is as strong as a man," Nicodin said, somewhat sheepishly. We boys all laughed but when he said, "Lina, you can defend your treasure until you give it away freely," we did not know what treasure Lina had. I wondered if she kept it in the small chest with the two iron handles and the lock, which was under her bed and opened by her only on Sunday afternoons when she had a few hours to herself, to take out her holiday shirt and aprons, also a flowered shawl when the weather was cold. The coat she wore in the winter hung behind the kitchen door, wrapped in a hempen bedsheet.

Lina was our friend although she could be very strict. We had almost twice as much freedom to make noise when we were alone with her as we had when Mrs. Bart was home, but if all of us ever shouted together, Lina would be up in arms at once. "One mouth at a time," she would say, stamping her foot.

∾∾∾∾∾∾∾∾∾∾∾∾

CHAPTER 20

HOME FOR MY CHRISTMAS VACATION, I FOUND A stranger in the village. It was Vasile Brad, a small fellow a year older than myself, brought to the village school by his father, Ion Brad, a friend of Uncle Gherasim's.

"Vasile comes from the mountains," Uncle Gherasim told me, as we looked at each other, Vasile and I, across the kitchen table. "As his father told the teacher, saying, 'Sir, this son of mine has set his heart on getting book learning, so I bring him into your hands,' that is why Vasile is here, and he likes my honey," Uncle Gherasim said. Vasile blushed. We had just finished licking the last remnant of honey off our plates.

"The teacher asked him his name. Then he said, 'You are nine years old,' because he judges a boy's age by height not by solidity," Uncle Gherasim said, chuckling. "But Vasile told him he was going on twelve and his father said, 'That's his right age, sir. Our first son. God's will, sir, for him to be a small creature and me and his mother quite tall.' I was with them, Peter, that is how I know.

"Then the teacher said, 'He will sit with the youngest, the beginners.'

" 'He is in your hands, sir, but as to being a beginner, with your leave, sir, that he is not,' my friend Ion said.

" 'Has he been to school before?' the teacher asked. To this question my friend answered with no few words. He said, 'No, sir, that he has not. It happened that a lad from our hamlet had his old schoolbooks that were lying idle, for he is beyond the age now, and this lad showed Vasile the letters from the first to the last and taught him to say them. Then he said to my boy, "You have a head for such things, I give you the books." Yes, he gave him a broken slate too.

" 'After that, my boy, obedient and tractable though he is, was not much help to me or to his mother. All day long he scribbled on the slate and when both sides were filled with such scribbling, packed like sheep in the fold, he wiped it all off and started again. If his mother said to him, "Rock your little sister, Vasile," the boy tied a string from the cradle to his ankle and, with your leave, sir, threw himself on his belly on the floor, and up and down went his foot, from the knee hinges, his hand scribbling and the cradle rocking.

" 'But now, you can bring sleep to an infant with rocking and can scare it away too, as often happened because Vasile forgot when to stop.

" 'Then he went to reading, at first slowly, until he got to rattle words off a page as fast as a hen picks oats from the floor.'

" 'So you can read and write, Vasile,' the teacher said. 'How do you spell horse?' he asked.

" 'Which horse, Mr. Teacher, for there are two kinds, mare and stallion,' Vasile said.

"For answer the teacher said, 'Leave Vasile here. Go home with the Lord.'

"So, you see, Peter, that is how they have a new pupil in our school, come from away up in the mountains," Uncle Gherasim said.

While he spoke, Vasile sat unmoving, watching Uncle Gherasim's face. Then, as if to test Uncle Gherasim's memory, he asked, "And what did my father say?"

"Well, Vasile, your father is a good man, he is an old friend of mine. He spoke as he should. He said, 'Thank you, sir,' to the teacher, then he patted you on the head and advised you in these words, 'Obey your teacher, be civil to your elders, and when you play with children play fairly. The Lord be with you. I am going home.' "

Vasile's face brightened in a broad smile, he brought his hands together and said, "That is just what he said."

We became friends. Uncle Gherasim told us his door was always open for Vasile and myself and there was honey, too, on the shelf to warm us up. He said honey was in cold weather the best fuel to put in the stomach. "It burns like dry birchwood," he said.

Of course dry birchwood burns fast with bright flames but it does not last like oak or beechwood. And that is what we told Uncle Gherasim.

"Therefore," he said, "you must take a good piece of bread with it. Honey for a quick fire, bread to make it last longer."

Vasile was put in the class with boys and girls his age and older, as a preliminary examination convinced teacher

Vlad that he belonged there legitimately. Age, intelligence, and knowledge entitled him to it, yes indeed, but not his stature.

Boys of nine were taller and sturdier than Vasile. Therefore, when the teacher brought him into the classroom and said to the pupils, "You have an additional classmate; his name is Vasile Brad," the children believed the teacher was putting them to shame with a dunce from the A-B-C class, for he had often told some of them they belonged with the first-grade dunces. And they resented his presence as the symbol of their humiliation.

Vasile took his place at the tail end of a long bench already crowded with twelve pupils, and twelve pairs of eyes cast him sullen looks. The children had made room for him while the teacher stood there, but as soon as he went to his desk they spread out and almost pushed Vasile off the bench. He said nothing, he only turned his head and scrutinized earnestly the row of twelve heads.

Then, to the amazement of his benchmates, he pulled out of a woolen bag—such as peasants carry their food in when traveling—three books, the broken slate, and a brand new notebook. Yes, and a new pencil he dug out from the bag too. He placed everything very carefully on the slanting desk in front of him; then he took from his belt a wood-handled penknife, opened it, and proceeded to sharpen his pencil. The two boys nearest to him watched with great interest. They could see that the knife was sharp, but what amazed them was Vasile's skill at handling it. A little fellow like that having a penknife. True, the knife was attached to the belt pocket with a string, but still, there it was, his own property. Whispering started along the length of the bench, heads turned, eyes opened wide, and there was a general stirring, as when a breeze strikes a row of cornstalks.

Teacher Vlad tapped the desk with his rattan, fixed his eyes on the particular bench and boomed, "Quiet." He called a name, Ioan Vintila. The boy sitting next to Vasile rose.

"Second Reader, page one hundred and twenty-one, *The Fox and the Stork*, read," the teacher commanded.

The boy found the page and started to read. Oh, what reading, Vasile said to himself, following in his own book, his finger moving along the line, from word to word, for Ioan read each word as if it had no connection whatever with the next. Like dropping stones into a well, Vasile thought.

Ioan had not gone more than two lines when teacher Vlad stopped him. "Enough," he shouted. He imitated the boy, then he said sternly, "Is this reading? Sit down!"

Next he called on Traian Dobrea. At least fifteen pupils, boys and girls, read—some more, some less, of *The Fox and the Stork*. Not one was allowed to finish the fable. Then he called, "Vasile Brad."

The little fellow jumped to his feet. "Read," teacher Vlad said, not too harshly. Vasile cleared his voice and began. Not loudly yet in a voice that carried each word clearly as if it were etched on the vibrant air. The children, despite their teacher's watchful eyes, turned their heads a little to see the new pupil, so much struck with wonderment they were.

But was this reading? each one asked himself, for they had never heard the like of it. The best reader in the class, Maria Avram, fourteen years old and with a golden voice, as the peasants said, read well, but this little chap simply talked naturally as if he were telling a story. He might as well not have looked at the book. They were all eager to hear what the teacher would say. They even expected him to rap on his desk and stop the little fellow, but teacher Vlad just sat there and let Vasile go on to the last word.

(When he told us the story he paid me a compliment saying, "You read as well as Vasile, Peter, and he is very good.")

The classroom was full of a gray, wintry light, in which everything was immersed like objects in heavy water. The light itself seemed to have body and weight. That is why, when Vasile stopped reading, the fable of *The Fox and the Stork* seemed to have taken form too, and become one with the rest of things in the classroom. "One could almost see the whole story, like it was alive," Ioan Vintila said, and the other boys agreed with him. A sort of miracle, really.

Now, when Vasile finished reading, the pupils were breathless, waiting to hear teacher Vlad comment. For a long moment he sat silent, unmoving. Then he spoke. But this time he did not burst out in his usual way, loud and commanding. His voice was deeper too and the words were not harsh but mellow, like ripe fruit, Maria Avram said.

"Vasile Brad, you read properly. Tell us now, how did you learn to read in this way?" he asked the boy.

Vasile blushed, embarrassed, and his voice quavered a little at the start, but then it got steady as he went on. "Where we live, up in the mountains, the winter is long. When we have light it is a tallow candle, but the evening comes early so too much candle would burn, therefore we

186

sit around the hearth, in the glow of the fire. We have neighbors who live not too far. They come over and sit with us. After they get warm one would tell a story, all of us listening. Then mother would ask Baba Sandra, who is very old and knows so many, to tell us one of her 'long, long tales.' I listened to all of them, from beginning to end, because after I grew up I never fell asleep in the middle of a story and asked mother the next day to tell me the rest. I heard Baba Sandra tell the same story three or four times, the one mother likes best, and mother said 'Baba Sandra is like a book, she never changes a word in the story.' So I think I learned from Baba Sandra how to read."

There was tittering in the classroom because the children found Vasile's explanation funny. Teacher Vlad smiled too. He silenced the pupils, told Vasile to sit down, and proceeded with arithmetic. Then came noon recess. The children, as soon as the teacher left the classroom, rushed into the hallway and out into the yard, like water from a dam. Vasile was carried with the rush.

But once in the yard they left him alone and started at their games—leapfrog, pole-jumping-with-sticks, and tug of war. The very small children, timidly huddled in one corner of the yard, watched the big ones. Many of these little boys and girls looked very forlorn. They shivered from the cold. One little girl began to cry and she wiped her nose on her coat sleeve, bending her head and lifting her arm so the two, her nose and sleeve, met midway. Then three others began to whimper, blowing on their cold hands to warm them.

Vasile walked over to them. "You will freeze altogether standing still," he said. The little children looked at him

187

with big, untrusting eyes, then bent their heads. "Look here, I will teach you a nice game, the wolf and the lamb. It will warm you up," he said.

The little girls huddled away from him in sullen silence. Vasile took from his shirt bosom two prunes. "The first one of you coming into the game will get these," he said, holding out the prunes in his palm. Two or three heads—wrapped in woolen shawls—turned around to look. None of the children came forward. Once more Vasile dug into his shirt bosom. This time he brought out a dried pear. "All of these," he said.

Now several of the bigger girls from Vasile's class came to see what was going on. They tittered, whispering among themselves. Then suddenly Maria Avram—she was the biggest in Vasile's class, the cleverest, too—straightened up and very earnestly said, "Aren't you ashamed, girls, laughing at him! He wants to play, don't you see?"

She meant to tease Vasile, but he said to her, "I know a nice game for them," and pointed at the group of little girls and boys.

"Then come and play with him," Maria said and, as Vasile was still holding out his hand, the prunes and dry pear on his palm, with a quick slap she struck them out of his hand. She ran off with her companions, all of them laughing.

Now the little ones laughed too. Vasile picked up the fruit and turned to them, saying, "She is a nice girl but this game is silly. My game is much better."

"Her game is nice, she is my sister," a small boy said, taking several steps toward Vasile. The little fellow was chunky, with a face round and red as an apple, his black

188

eyes brightly intelligent. In his heavy woolen coat he looked as if he could roll instead of walk.

"Well then, let us play her game," Vasile said. He held out the fruit on the palm of his hand. The little boy made a dash, trying to knock it out of Vasile's hand. But Vasile dodged him cleverly and let him roll by like a ball. The little girls laughed and moved closer. Then suddenly several of them ran forward and, in the melee, one of them knocked the fruit to the ground. So the game got in full swing, and noisy it was too, with laughter and shrieks, and when the bell rang all the little ones were warm, their faces glowing. They trooped behind Vasile into the schoolhouse, like so many chicks following a mother hen.

That very day Vasile got his nickname, Closca, which means mother hen. After school he walked to his aunt's home, where he would stay during the school term, right here in our village, miles away from his parents' hut. Several small children walked along with him a good part of the way. The big boys teased Vasile with his nickname and Traian Savu ran up to him and, pretending to show him something, tripped him. The children laughed at his clumsy fall. Vasile got up and instead of crying, for he did hurt his knee, he laughed too. Traian felt more silly than proud at his prank. "The Closca is tough," he said to his friends.

By the time the first snow fell Vasile had become the favorite of the little children, Uncle Gherasim told me. He was their game leader and storyteller. Often during recess they would all sit along the walls of the hall, listening to Vasile spin and spin a yarn as long as it was exciting. Dragons, princesses, winged horses, golden forests where trees and shrubs and all growth were gold, even the flowing streams were liquid gold and so too the fishes and the birds and butterflies. Of such and other marvels, one more wonderful than the other, Vasile told them. Entrancing stories. It even happened that the bell rang and the children did not hear it. How could they when under the spell of such wonders?

But the noise of the bigger pupils and their appearance in the hall brought Vasile's listeners back to reality. Oh, what an awakening that was for the little ones. Rude and disappointing. The story had to be stopped just when they were holding their breath because the fairy prince was fighting the dragon of the Crystal Palace.

In the winter, with snow on the streets, houses, trees, and fences, our village became itself a fairyland. The air had a tang of mountain freshness and wood smoke so, when you breathed it, you felt light, ready to run and jump and shout with gladness. You felt eager for adventure. A battle with snowballs, one group of children against another, posted as you thought soldiers would be in war—that was in your mind and in the minds of all the children.

In the classroom, where the air is warm and heavy, you attended to your lessons, but your thoughts flew out now and again into fairyland. Who should wonder then that at noon recess you ran out with the rest of the children and before you blinked twice with your eyes you were in the heat of battle? Yes, but in war, to conduct battles there must be a leader. The smaller children had such a leader, this chap Vasile, who must have learned a lot about wars from those stories he knew. He formed two armies, on one side the girls, the other side boys, and he the general of both armies, leader and umpire at the same time.

190

He saw to it that both sides did bravely, but fairness, too, had to be abided by. That was the umpire's business. Your ammunition consisted of snowballs, but you must not make them too hard lest they become dangerous. And you must not aim at your enemy's head. By accident you might strike him in the head, therefore your snowball should be soft.

Well, this day the war was on, both sides doing their best and Vasile, general-umpire, gave orders now to this rank, now to the other, trying to win a fair victory for the most valiant side. Being in the very center of the battle, Vasile got hit with balls from both armies, accidentally of course. He was covered with slush, his face was red, and he was so warm he threw off his coat right into the snow.

The line of fighters swayed, as fortunes of war would have it, then suddenly came to a hand-to-hand clash. In the melee, the general-umpire was thrown off his feet. Soldiers of both armies trampled on him and fell on top of him, squirming in the snow.

With the leader downed, who could tell how the war would have ended, had the bell not put a stop to it? The fallen soldiers got to their feet and the general picked himself up too, looking more like a snowman than the leader of two opposing armies. His soldiers could not help laughing at him even while they helped shake the snow off his clothes.

Vasile picked up his coat and marched into the schoolhouse, followed by his many battlers. He had proved himself a good leader in every way, even to the point of falling when he could not help it.

By Christmas our whole village knew Vasile, because the children spoke about him at home and they pointed him out to their elders when he passed within sight of their heavily frosted window in which one pane was kept clear. "Nobody can live in a blind house," the women said.

But his classmates, the bigger lads—even the girls—resented him more than ever. He was the black sheep of the entire school. If at least he had had the natural stature of his age, then it would have been easier for them to endure his fine mind and good nature, although even then they would have resented the great difference between his and their ability to learn. As it was, this mere mite of a fellow, and with such a head, was too much for them, for they were put to shame by him not only at school but in their own homes. A father would say to his son, "Now, how is this, you, a big lad that you are, lagging behind a little chap like this Vasile, whom I hear praised even by his reverence, the priest? Don't your cheeks burn from shame?" Actually these are the words Traian Savu heard from his father, and his cheeks did burn then.

Christmas is a great and happy holiday. In our village, as throughout all of Romania, it is celebrated in the old, old way with carols, Herod and the three Magi, the Star, and with cheering songs of felicitations, which the children perform and sing, going from house to house. Every household makes preparations for this joyous day. Housewives bake small rolls, sprinkled with raisins and sweetened with honey or sugar, bring up apples from the cellar—those who have such fruit in the dead of winter—and dried prunes and nuts, and the well to do count out a few pieces of copper coin. All these for the children, who keep

192

coming all day long, bringing cheer, frozen hands, and a bag to carry the presents.

At this Christmas there was in our village an additional child, this Vasile Brad. I was home for the holidays, but his vacation had not yet started so Vasile worked every day after school, until bedtime, making stars. The kitchen in his aunt's house became a workshop. Aunt Susana was good about it, giving the place over to Vasile. She only grumbled a little when so many children came to watch Vasile at his work that she could hardly move about. Then she would say, "Now don't you cry, any of you, if these feet of mine step on you, for you are like weeds in a neglected garden bed."

The little tots said they wouldn't cry and they crowded together as best they could, out of her way. And Vasile kept at his work. First he constructed the wooden frames from strips of shingle, then he pasted the gold or silver paper on them. Some stars were gold, others silver. Vasile liked variety. And besides, he said, "You just look up and you will see that there are golden and silver stars in heaven too."

Vasile taught the song of the Star to the children and showed them how this holy emblem must be held. And the carrier had to twist and move his hand in a certain way, while they were singing, so that the star should give the impression of twinkling.

Only small children go around with a star; the bigger boys dress up to impersonate Herod and the Magi. According to age, Vasile belonged with the bigger boys, but none would have him. Therefore he organized six groups of the smaller ones, five children in each group.

Christmas day came. The morning was dark and very cold. The blanket of heavy clouds hung so low that the cross on the church steeple touched it. But all the children were gathered in the courtyard at Vasile's at eight o'clock in the morning. Vasile gave one star to each group, keeping the last for his own, and they set out. By noon they had sung at more than half the houses of the village, for the groups had gone in different directions and met in front of our house at the hour of twelve. The bag carriers showed with pride the gifts they had gathered.

Snow was falling. Already a thin blanket of fresh snow lay over that which was packed and frozen. The children were in the act of holding a consultation whether they should go home for dinner or have a quick luncheon from the provisions in their bags, and continue on their happy errand that much sooner.

Suddenly there appeared three groups of the older boys, dressed up as Herod and the Magi. They looked strange in their garments pasted with colored paper, and all of them wearing gold crowns over their sheepskin caps, Herod's crown being the tallest. And each had a sword in a silver scabbard dangling in the snow. Of course, sword and scabbard were made of wood, but the silver paper covering transformed them to appear what they were not. At any rate, a sword is a weapon even if made of wood.

The oriental splendor of their outfit made these boys very unnatural in the swirling snow. The little children laughed and shrieked with amusement.

At the head of this regal procession was Ioan Savu, a lanky, quick-tempered lad, who for months had had a sullen grudge against Vasile. To him, the little fellow's excellence in school had been an affront from the very start.

Even the fact that Vasile had been given a place beside him he interpreted as unfair on the part of teacher Vlad, whose intention must have been to show him up for a numskull. And it happened also that because of his resentment, Ioan became duller at his lessons after Vasile was placed near him, as if this little chap, owing to his unusual brightness, clouded his mind.

And now, hearing the children laugh and shout, Ioan took their hilarity for derision incited by Vasile. Rage flared up in him. He drew his sword, turned to his companions and shouted, "The enemy! Charge!"

The other lads, ready for play, snatched out their swords and, led by Ioan, made the assault upon the little children. Whooping and yelling they came, brandishing their swords.

The little fellows took fright. They crowded against our big gate. Had the gate been open they would have rushed into our courtyard as into a fortress. But Nicodin had fastened the gate so that we should not be disturbed during our noon meal. So, the gate being closed, all the little children could do was to give way to their fright in shrieks.

Vasile, however, stepped forward. Was he not their leader? And then, too, he believed that Ioan and his fellows were merely playing a prank to frighten the children. Entering into the spirit of what he took to be a game, Vasile held out the star he was carrying like a shield, and cried, "Halt, Herod! Thou shalt not touch these innocent children. The star is mightier than thy wicked sword."

Had Ioan been in his senses, the affair would have remained nothing more than a game, but Ioan was angry, and his anger grew worse at Vasile's challenge. With a furious blow of his sword he struck the star out of Vasile's

195

hand, and next he made a lunge at Vasile's breast. Luckily, the heavy coat prevented the sword from reaching further than Vasile's skin, but the thrust was violent enough to throw him off his feet. He fell on his back.

Ioan was ready to strike again but Vasile gave a gasp, tried to raise his arms which suddenly dropped limp, and he moved no more. By this time the other boys were upon the scene. They stood around the prostrate boy, a silly crowd with their swords in hand and stupid, questioning looks in their eyes.

"What's happened to him?" one of them asked Ioan.

"He fell on his back," Ioan stammered. He was livid from fright.

"Ioan pierced him with his sword," several of the small children cried. They ventured closer. One of them started to wail and soon others began to cry. Ioan stared at the little fellows then he shouted, "Be quiet, wet snouts, or I will chop your heads off." But instead of making a move, as the children cried more violently now, he stood there petrified.

"Help him to his feet," one of the Magi said. "Ioan, give me a hand." He bent over Vasile and lifted him by the shoulder. Vasile's head fell back.

"My God!" the lad said, dropping the burden in the snow. He jumped away as one threatened by a snake.

"What is it?" his companions asked, crowding back.

For answer, the boy who tried to lift Vasile turned to Ioan and said, "You have killed him."

"You are lying, you are lying. He is not dead. I have not killed him. It is a game we were playing," Ioan shouted at the top of his voice. "I will show you." He knelt down, took snow in both hands and started rubbing Vasile's face with it. But now he was crying. His tears streamed down his face and dropped on Vasile's head. Then, in a voice broken by sobs, he started to call, "Vasile! Listen to me, Vasile. Here, wake up. Get up, the ground is cold. Get up." At his point he started slapping Vasile's cheeks. Very rapidly he kept at it, calling to Vasile to wake up, his voice now stifled with sobs, then rising to a shriek of fright. But Vasile did not move.

"Leave him alone then," several boys said. They took hold of Ioan and pulled him away.

"But he is not dead," Ioan cried, trying to free himself. "No! he is not dead. He is not, he is trying to frighten me. He is trying to kill me with fright."

The boys had a task holding him, for he struggled madly. He tried to bite too, and there was no way of subduing the fellow but to throw him down and pin his arms and legs to the ground.

The smaller children came and surrounded Vasile. They pleaded with him to rise as if he were not dead. Each one in turn and several at one time begged him to rise. Vasile did not move. That awful stillness of his and his eyes only half closed proved too much for one little chap. He suddenly bent down and struck Vasile on the face. "Sit up," he screeched. "Yes, get up now," others cried. They all became angry with their leader for prolonging their uncertainty. Some of them kicked him, others pulled at his clothes, and some laughed at the antics of their companions. Before long the whole crowd was in ferment, raising a clamor unbecoming to the festive holiday.

They were so engaged in this unusual behavior that Dr.

Anastase came upon the scene unnoticed. He stopped the horse and from the sleigh he called to the children, inquiring what they were about.

The children hushed at once and drew away a few steps. They pointed at the ground. Dr. Anastase jumped off the sleigh and rushed over. "This lad is dead," he said. "What's happened?"

At that moment Ioan succeeded in breaking free from his companions. He ran off and soon was lost to sight in the swirling snow.

Dr. Anastase carried Vasile's corpse to the boy's aunt. The children followed the doctor's sleigh. At the gate he ordered them about their business. He spoke curtly. The children ran away.

Susana rushed out from the house. The doctor was carrying Vasile in his arms. She threw up her arms, then she clasped her hands. "What happened? Oh, poor boy. Oh, good sir, what happened?" she asked, now running ahead of the doctor to open the door.

"He fractured his skull falling on a stone," the doctor said. He placed the boy gently on the hearth bed, in the kitchen.

"Poor lad. He was a dove amongst hawks," Vasile's aunt said. "Too good for this world, and that smartness of his irked the children. If only his body had been as strong as his mind." She spoke these words in the manner of mourners, half talk and half chanting.

"The fall killed him. Fractured skull," the doctor said.

"Misfortune comes in its own way," the woman lamented. "I have no heart to take care of his remains. I will call a neighbor," she said. But when she was ready to leave the house, several women came, and upon entering the room they started to weep.

The doctor left. The women washed Vasile's body, dressed him in his Sunday clothes, and laid him out on the bench. They put a copper coin in his hands and folded them on his chest. The aunt fastened a wax taper into a wooden candlestick, lit it, and placed it at the head of the boy. "Who will carry the sad message to his parents?" she kept lamenting.

The news about the misfortune spread quickly. The children carried it and the whole village heard about what had happened to poor Vasile. The children told that it was Ioan Savu who caused the boy's death. But where was Ioan? He had run away from the fatal scene, but where? Nobody knew. Evening was falling and he did not get home. His father had waited for him, sitting with his head in his hands in the glow of the fire on the hearth and giving no answer to his wife's questions.

When it was getting dark, the man rose, put on his sheepskin coat and cap, and walked out of the house.

"Bring him home, Aron," his wife called after him.

"As the Lord will ordain," Aron answered and was gone. He went straight to Susana, Vasile's aunt. The women made room for him to approach the dead. Aron crossed himself, bowed his head over the corpse and said, "God rest your soul in peace, Vasile. Forgive my son and pray to our good Lord for him." Again he crossed himself; then, turning to the women, he said, "Has word gone to his parents?"

"They have no word of the misfortune," Vasile's aunt said.

"It is God's will then that I should be the messenger of this sad news," Aron said. "I will set out at once."

The women gave him a lantern to light his way. "Go with the Lord," they said.

Early next morning Aron and Vasile's father arrived. The tall, gaunt mountaineer approached the bier on tip-toe, bowed forward as one eager to behold something dear to him. At the foot of the bier he stopped. For a long time his face remained in blank immobility. The women who had chanted laments until then now became silent. None stirred. The stillness itself seemed dead. Only the flame of the taper appeared alive, incongruously bright in the dim chill of the dead chamber. After what seemed to the women a long time, the boy's father spoke unexpectedly.

"You have left us, son. The scythe of death has mowed you down. Son, you were too good for this world. The Lord has given you too much mind and too little flesh and bone. Your body was too weak a shelter for your soul. The Lord called your soul into His heavenly kingdom. The lot of such as we is hard in this earthly life. And you were a lamb strayed among wolves. God rest your soul in eternal peace." He crossed himself, bowed his head upon the foot of the bier, then straightened up and retired to sit on the bench against the wall.

Aron Savu followed him and sat down beside him. After a long silence he said, "As I told you already, I want to make amends for my son's unfortunate fault. You can't doubt, as I can't, that the misfortune came by accident. Still, it is my duty to make amends. Tell me, what shall I do?"

The mountaineer kept his eyes on his son's face. It was serene, beautiful in the deep sleep of death. Without averting his gaze, he said quietly, "What amends could you make, friend? My son is dead."

"True, your poor son is dead, Ion, very true. There I can't interfere. But we are alive, Ion, so, to lighten your burden in some way, that is how I mean," Aron said.

"Is sorrow such a thing you can divide it?" Ion said.

"No, certainly not. Every man's sorrow is his own," Aron said mournfully. For a long time he remained silent. Then, his face lighting up, he said, "I will pay for the interment, the priest, the deacon, and for ringing the church bells. For everything I will pay, for the coffin too. Agree with me, Ion, for my own peace."

They spoke so quietly the women could not hear what they were saying. Discretion kept them at a distance from the two men weighed down by this calamity.

So the men carried on their murmured conversation until at length they reached an agreement. Aron proposed to furnish the coffin and the flour for the funeral rolls which would be distributed to children and the poor. He left soon and by noon returned with a horse and a contraption fastened to the saddle. Then he brought the coffin on his shoulders and helped Ion place Vasile's corpse in it.

"Then we shall not have the funeral here?" Susana asked.

"We mean to have him near us. Our little cemetery, on top of the hill, is a good place," Ion said.

Now Susana wept more. She chanted a mournful lament and a farewell to this angel of a boy. "You are leaving a great emptiness in my heart, Vasile, dear Vasile," she chanted.

It would have been a great event to have the funeral

services held in her little house. Since twenty years ago, when her husband was buried, no important event of any kind had taken place in her house. No birth, no baptism, no wedding, and no funeral feast. Quiet and monotony had come to lodge with her and never left. Vasile, her nephew, had brought new life and the glowing light of youth, and now he was taken away from her by a cruel fate that deprived her even of the sorrowful but important occurrence, the funeral service, the interment, with the procession to the cemetery, and the return from there in a group of women who would say words of consolation to her. Gloom and desolation would return again into her little house and remain with her until her last breath.

But fate relented a little. The second day of Christmas is observed by the peoples of Greek Orthodox faith as a holiday nearly as sacred as the first day. And so, Susana had some consolation. She summoned all the school children to form a procession to accompany their dead schoolmate from her house to the outskirts of the village. And she asked teacher Vlad to honor the "dear dead" with his presence at this farewell.

More than a hundred children marched, two by two, behind the horse on whose back the coffin was fastened. Vasile's father led the horse and Aron walked at its side, steadying every now and again the contraption to which the coffin was fastened.

Mother allowed me to go with teacher Vlad, so, walking by his side, we led the column of children. When the procession halted, quite a little distance beyond the outskirts of the village, teacher Vlad pronounced a short farewell speech in honor of "our brilliant pupil and friend, Vasile Brad."

He led the children in singing, "Lord Light His Way," and sang with them in his deep droning voice.

It was a sad parting. I stood there with the teacher, watching the two men, one leading the horse, the other walking beside it, move slowly across the plain and follow the road on the river bank. The children had broken rank and soon they broke their silence and were on the point of engaging in a snow battle when teacher Vlad turned around and assumed control again.

But on the way home they lost completely the air of solemnity which they had preserved coming. Myself, I was following in imagination Vasile, sleeping in the coffin slung over the back of the horse, and the two men, wondering how soon night would fall upon them. And I was sad all the way home.

CHAPTER 21

〇〇〇〇〇〇〇〇〇〇〇〇〇

FATHER WAS FOR PUNISHING IOAN SAVU PROPERLY. "That boy is a murderer," he said. But mother said that since Vasile was dead and his father had forgiven Ioan, we should thank God for his infinite mercy and wisdom. "God inspired the mountaineer to forgive this boy," she said.

"And who inspires me, Barbara, to want him punished?" father asked angrily.

"It will be the Lord, if you ask Him," mother said gently.

"O, good Lord, inspire me," father said, but there was no supplication in his tone of voice. He did not slam any of the doors, but by the time he got to the gate he could no longer observe the rule. He slammed the gate behind him.

Mother asked me about our procession and when I told her that teacher Vlad made a farewell speech, she praised him. And she said that it was a very sad happening but it was not an accident. "Everything that comes to pass is preordained, my dear little soul," she said. "Nothing, not a feather falling out of a bird's wing, is unknown to God."

204

I dared not ask her why, then, father wanted Ioan Savu punished, because we were not allowed to probe into the why of our parents' opinions. But as I had a small boil on the back of my neck, which mother had bandaged, having applied a home remedy to bring it to a head, I could not help wondering if the sacred Laws of Heaven had pre-arranged it for me. And then I came to admit that my boil could not have come by itself. Boils were not floating in the air, like specks of dust, for instance, therefore I got it by the Heavenly decree, I told myself.

Uncle Gherasim also believed in predestination. He called it fate. "You see, Peter," he said, "when you do your very best to accomplish something as you have planned, and it turns out in failure, that means that fate had decided it so."

I could ask Uncle Gherasim any question that came to my mind, so I said, "But how does fate know beforehand what I am planning to do tomorrow, Uncle Gherasim?"

"Well, Peter, it would not be fate if it did not know," Uncle Gherasim said, "and if I knew how it does know, then I would have its knowledge too." He chuckled and I made no head or tail of his explanation. But I asked no more questions on this subject because when Uncle Gherasim chuckled it was a sign that while he could talk about the particular matter he could bring no light upon it.

What puzzled me at the moment was the question of life and death. The death of Vasile was accidental. He had not been sick nor was he old. Of course, there was fate to take into account. But which of the two did fate serve, life or death? That is what puzzled me. For it was always in cases of some misfortune that the people brought in fate. And certainly, death was the greatest of all misfor-

205

tunes in my opinion. Could it be that fate was in some way related to the devil, since it was the devil who plagued human beings?

So I asked Uncle Gherasim why there was a devil. Uncle Gherasim took a few puffs from his pipe, looking at me earnestly, then said, "Peter, if we believe that something exists, then it does exist. But where does it exist? In our mind. To believe in something is to plant that thing in our mind. And the longer we hold that belief, the deeper its roots will grow."

Father had said often that Uncle Gherasim was a deep thinker. What he was telling me now must be deep thinking, I thought to myself. So terribly deep that I could not understand it at all.

"But, Uncle Gherasim," I ventured further, "Is there a devil?"

"We have believed for a long time that there is," he said.

"So the roots are deep," I said proudly. That was all I could understand.

"Yes, Peter, the roots are very deep," Uncle Gherasim said. He smiled but did not chuckle.

And what did I learn from it all? I learned that the belief in the existence of the devil had very deep roots in our mind. But I still did not know if there really was a devil or not. Did I believe there was? Yes, I did. And I became frightened, thinking of the roots that would grow deeper and deeper in my mind.

As to life and death, this idea about the deep roots chased them out of my mind. It was indeed terrifying to know that once you believed in something the belief would strike deeper and deeper roots in your mind. And of course everybody in the village believed there was a devil. The priest believed it too. He often mentioned him in his sermons. Once I heard him say that the devil was tempting Jesus, and the Savior said, "Get thee behind me, Satan."

There were some, like old Susana, who said they had the misfortune of seeing "the black one" with their mortal eyes. But when Popa Radu was told about it he roared with laughter and then said, "As to their eyes they are mortal enough, but were they sober?"

Mother turned away and crossing herself murmured, "God save us from the evil."

At that time Popa Radu and father discussed at length the superstitions of our peasants. They agreed that all superstitions had their roots in our fear of the unknown. And, to obviate this or that evil which threatened or actually fell upon some person, the folk devised various forms of incantation and soothsaying.

Popa Radu told us the story about his beadle coming to him one early morning livid with fright. "He was putting things in order in the church. It was just getting light. The poor man was by the altar. As he turned around he looked up and saw on the choir balcony what he said was the devil, looking down at him from up there. 'Black he is, your reverence, with horns on,' he panted. And he would not go back unless I went with him, which I had to do, as there was work to be done before our services that morning. I went. We walked into the church, the poor man holding on to my sleeve. I looked up but there was nothing. Then suddenly we heard sharp sounds of steps. The beadle fell into my arms. 'There he is,' he gasped.

" 'Then we must see him,' I said. 'God beware, your

reverence, not I. I will prostrate myself here, on the sacred floor of our church, and close my eyes,' he said. With that he ran in front of the altar and threw himself on the floor. I walked up a few steps and met my black buck. It had strayed into the church and had climbed up there.

"'Come down, you devil,' I said at the top of my voice. The creature clattered down the steps and ran out of the church. I walked over to Gheorghe. 'Come and see the black one,' I said.

"'Have mercy, reverend father, I heard him,' he said. I lifted him to his feet. 'Come! It is black, but it is not the devil, it is my buck,' I said. And I took him to the door. The buck was there, grazing in the churchyard. Gheorghe saw him. But soon the whole village knew that he had seen the devil whom I had chased out of the church, as, being anointed, I had power over him. It took me a long time to convince some of the people that what Gheorghe saw was my buck. No devil will dare set foot in the house of the Lord, I told them. Yet, to this day there are some women in our village who believe Gheorghe. They say that I might be right about the devil not daring to enter the church in his devil's shape, but taking the shape of my poor buck, he deceived even me and overcame the holy ban of the church against him."

During the narration of this story, mother sat spellbound, her eyes glued on Popa Radu. And when father burst out laughing, she glanced at him reprovingly. Then she said, "Poor Gheorghe," and sighed.

"Poor imbecile," father said, and mimicked mother's sighing.

As I walked home from Uncle Gherasim's, it was get-

208

ting dark. Popa Radu's story came to my mind and before I knew it I broke into a run and never stopped until I was inside our courtyard, the gate closed behind me.

"Where have you been so late, my little soul?" mother asked me.

"I was at Uncle Gherasim's, mother," I said.

"Tomorrow he is coming to have dinner with us. You are fond of him too," she said, and kissed me. Then she lit the lamp, the big ceiling lamp, and said, "Good evening." I went to my favorite corner where the bench had a frieze blanket on it, folded several times to make a soft seat, and being left alone, the smell of kerosene brought to mind the past of a few years.

My first recollection of a penetrating scent was the smell of kerosene. It was not unpleasant although different from the smell of fresh earth or baking bread. I recall very clearly that winter evening. Father came in with his mustaches white with frost. Even his eyebrows and eyelashes were white.

Mother was lighting our big table lamp with the porcelain shade, which to me looked like an enormous cap that would fit the head of the giant about whom Uncle Gherasim told us the most fantastic stories. In my mind I likened the shade to a cap because father had an astrakhan fur cap which he wore in the winter pulled down over his ears and forehead, so that it touched his eyebrows.

There is another smell that I remember from those days and it recalls to me enchanting winter evenings. It is the smell of a sheepskin coat impregnated with heavy cold— Uncle Gherasim's coat, an enormous thing that he hung on a peg behind the door where, to me, it looked like a great furry animal trying to reach up to the whitewashed ceiling.

On the long winter evenings father would read aloud from the paper or some stories from the calendar, which every year had a few stories that my sister Irina and I could hear and enjoy. The calendar was a voluminous book, a treasure of information for the rural folk. Mother gleaned in its wide field precious knowledge about plants and we children delighted in the pictures illustrating the nature of each month, and then the stories. There were folk tales too, fantastic and beautiful—but none of them were like the stories Uncle Gherasim told us. Uncle Gherasim always started with the words "Once upon a time . . ." and those words opened a vista for my imagination into the furthest past and gave me a feeling that our life was indeed eternal. For, after all, if my fancy carried me so far into the past, I felt that I was actually there, and as to the future, that for me was endless. The days that passed were not carrying away parts of my life; they were tiny wavelets in the endless stream of the future, whose flow was from one eternity to another. To me, as a child, eternity was as real as our stone barn, under the eaves of which swallows built their earthen nests.

When father opened the paper, settling himself to begin reading, Cilly, one of our three cats, always jumped onto the table to make a rest for the paper, under which she lay purring, while my father's voice droned out the news for mother and some neighbors who were visiting in time to hear it. The rustling of the paper in father's hand was a signal to Cilly. We never knew how this cat got the

210

habit of serving as a rest for the paper, but there it was, and she never failed in it.

We children were not in the least interested in the news father read, but we enjoyed the ritual, for it was part of the home life as much as the three daily meals.

Actually, every day was a kind of holiday for Irina and me because a holiday is a day of joy and we had ways of turning little tasks into pleasure, but the outstanding holidays were the days when Uncle Gherasim came and closed them with stories. And what stories they were! Fairy queens whose beauty had no comparison with anything earthly. One was like the evening star, another like the full moon, another like the day awakening from the embrace of night, and one there was so resplendent that mortal eyes could not look into her face as we could not look into the sun. Then there were dragons with seven heads, furies who spat fire, real fire that scorched everything in its path. But none of these monsters could stand up against a prince charming and his wonder horse which had two pairs of wings, the gift of speech, and wisdom deeper than that of the wise men of antiquity. Without the aid of such a horse, the bravest prince charming of all would have been unable to cope with those terrifying foes. Practically every prince charming in Uncle Gherasim's stories set out in quest of love, the love embodied in a fairy queen or princess. And the dragons and the furies always tried to thwart his purpose.

Other great days for us were those when, as soon as it got dark and the lamps in the house were lit, the young people of the village would come. These were the evenings for shelling beans and peas, or stripping mounds of duck and chicken feathers. These were the evenings which helped mother to put away large quantities of beans and peas, and supply us with feathers for pillows and feather beds. We had so many pillows that the bed in one of the rooms—which was seldom used and only by a visitor who could not be put up elsewhere in the house—was piled up with pillows to the ceiling.

At these bees there was much gaiety. The girls and young men sang, teased each other good-naturedly, and closed the evening with dancing. On these occasions Irina and I were allowed to stay up—until I fell asleep on the bench to wake up in the morning in my bed.

Mother always told me that I was put to bed by one of the girls whom I particularly liked, Ileana, the daughter of One-eyed John. She was tall and graceful and very beautiful. She was fifteen years old when I was five, and the gossips had not yet invented the horrible tale that she had sold her soul to the devil for the great beauty and uncommon cleverness she had. No girl in the village could embroider like Ileana, and there was no woman who could spin wool, hemp, or linen into as fine and even a thread. And what a voice Ileana had!

When we had visitors from the city mother always invited Ileana to come and sing for us. When she came she brought joy with her as other persons bring presents. Her being with us was a gift. We loved her and she was my first love after mother. Once, when father teased me about Veturia, Dr. Bran's daughter, I told them all that I would marry Ileana. This happened when Irina was sick and Dr. Bran brought Veturia with him when he came. Dr. Bran was our family doctor, and Veturia was his only daughter. She was one year older than I; I was five years

212

old and she six, when her father brought her to us for the first time. It was a sunny winter day. Irina had some swelling on her throat, which the old women said was nothing at all and could be cured in a blinking if a twin boy or girl would bite it three times and repeat a particular incantation as many times.

Mother was ready to have the remedy tried, but father protested. He said, "Now, Barbara, you might have some savage bite off Irina's swelling, but you can't cure a fever with bites, and Irina has a fever."

It is very likely that my sister did have a slight fever, for we both ran fevers easily. But mother made light of it. She said that we were simply overheated from something we ate. Generally that was true, but father used to poke fun at her for considering us as nothing more than stoves or bake ovens. "You put fuel into them and presto, they get overheated," he said.

"They are not stoves and the people here are not savages, and if you want Dr. Bran to come, tell him to come with you tomorrow when you return from the city," mother said. "And for now I'll just keep her throat wrapped in cloth."

Dr. Bran could not come until the following day. He drove himself and Veturia in a very fashionable sleigh, drawn by his black horse, which I admired greatly.

Veturia was wrapped in a large buffalo rug. She wore a fur cap and a fur coat; on her feet were felt boots. Father carried her into the house in his arms. He set her down in the middle of the room and called to Irina and me, who were at the far end of the room by the window. "Come children, and greet this little fairy," he said.

Irina had a way of pouting when she was displeased

213

with something. She was a big girl for her nine years and since I, her brother, was four years younger, she considered herself almost grown up.

We went dutifully and greeted Veturia with the customary "welcome to us," and shook hands with her. Veturia merely smiled a little but said nothing. She seemed embarrassed and stood there looking now at Irina, now at me. Her face was very red from the cold, which made her blue eyes look like two shiny beads.

Mother took off her cap and then I saw Irina's eyes grow big in wonder. Veturia's hair was a mass of golden curls. My sister had raven black hair and eyes as black.

"That is why father called her 'fairy,' for that hair of hers," she said to me later when she was going to bed. I gave my bed to Veturia, and slept on the sofa in the dining room.

After they left the next day, Irina complained to mother that her neck was too much swaddled in cloth when "that little girl came."

Father laughed and said, "She did not come for you, she came for your brother. He is going to marry her when he grows up." They all looked at me.

I lowered my head and was ready to cry, but I managed to say, "I shall not marry her."

"No? Whom will you marry then?" father asked.

"Ileana," I said promptly. And then I did cry because even mother laughed, and she never had laughed before when father teased me. And he also embarrassed me when he boasted of having a son like me. It is true that I had a big head for my age, but why did he have to prove it to his friends by jamming his astrakhan cap on my head? Then he would pull it off, some times pulling my hair with it, and with his finger tap the top of my head saying, "And it is not empty."

Father was rough even when he thought he was gentle. He was a very strong man and the hairiest I have ever seen. Often in the winter he would go out naked to his waist, and rub his arms, chest, and neck with snow and come into the house puffing with pleasure and saying how good it felt.

A few times he tried to have me go out with him and get myself "washed with snow" as he said, but mother said no.

It was wonderful how a *no* from mother would stop him. And mother never said *no* sharply or loudly. She just uttered the word naturally, but it had a finality in it the way she said it. And always father would look at her as though a door had been shut in his face.

Father had a reputation for gruffness just as mother had for gentleness. He showed this especially in the winter. It was because he could not work off his choler, mother said, as in the other seasons when he did the garden, from early spring until the cabbages were harvested. He was also very sensitive to odors and could not endure the smell of tallow or fish oil on boots. In the dead of winter when the severe colds were on, the peasants who wore *opinci** would smear their feet with tallow and swaddle them in woolen cloth. Often, when a peasant so protected against frostbite would come to see father, mother, herself, would bring him into father's room, which was his office. She would rush to father and whisper in his ear, "Don't scare

---

* A form of sandal, made of one piece of sole leather, curved up on the sides, in front, and back to the shape of the foot, and held with leather strips wound around the ankle.

the poor man away, because I shall have to bring him back. He smells of tallow."

Without a word father would jump up and open one window wide. Then he would shout at the man standing in the middle of the room, "Come here. What is your complaint? Tell me in a few words." And he would crook his nose with a grimace.

We always had myrrh and incense in our home. As soon as the man was out of the house, father would open the door and shout, "Bring the hearth shovel with hot coals." He would sprinkle myrrh or incense on the hot coals and fumigate the room, then fumigate the kitchen and hallway too. On such days our house smelt like the church. If Irina and I had been away during the incident we would know as soon as we stepped into the house what had happened.

But despite his gruffness, father was liked by the people. They considered him a wizard in matters of law and came from distant villages to consult him. He never took money from the poor for his services, but he made them pay for the necessary fiscal stamps. Every scrap of paper that had any legal matter on it had to be stamped. If the client had no money, or not enough for these stamps, father would scold him properly. "Don't you know that much? I am not printing those damned pieces of paper myself. And I don't keep any in stock."

Mother would then come in, for when father scolded he could be heard in the entire house. "He has no stamps and no money to buy them," father would say in the same tone of voice.

"Come, I will tell you where to buy them," mother would say to the wretched man.

"How will he buy them, he has no money, Barbara?" father would ask, a little more quietly now.

"Bucur will trust him for a day," mother would answer. Bucur had the tobacco and stamp license. Father would shrug his shoulders and wave the man out, but mother would ask the man in the hallway how much money he needed, give it to him, and send him for the stamps.

Father pretended not to know about it, but he did know it, although mother insisted that Bucur had a heart of gold and trusted a poor man. How father knew was that he had asked Bucur, who told him that he never trusted anybody when it came to stamps. He even told father, confidentially, that those pieces of paper were a plague on the poor people, a devilish invention, and he did not like to handle them nor would he if it were not that the license for tobacco included them.

CHAPTER 22

⊙⊙⊙⊙⊙⊙⊙⊙⊙⊙⊙⊙⊙

THE ROMANIAN PEASANT IS GENEROUS. THOUGH HE
has little he gives to those who have less. And he always
strives to show gratitude for a favor. Those from whom
father took no money returned with a gift of some kind;
a few eggs, a hen, a basket of grapes or other fruit. Those
who had sheep would bring us a cheese in the fall. We
even received wood, brought in bundles that were tied
and hung on the two sides of the horse like sheaves of
rye, the rope that held them stretched across the saddle.

There is no sadder animal than a poor horse belonging
to a poor peasant, unless it is his dog. But the dog livens
up, wags his tail, and even jumps a little when he is given
a piece of bread or a bone. The horse, however, takes the
apple or a handful of grass and munches it indifferently as
if to say, "This won't change my lot. You gave it to me, I
accept it, but my days will drag on in misery to the end."

In the winter the peasant's horse would grow a shaggy
fur, but even that could not hide the lean body of the
animal. We all had great pity for such horses. Once on a
cold winter day a man came with a load of wood. We had

218

just come out in the yard, Irina and I, when he arrived. As the man was lifting the wood off the horse's back, mother came out. She walked over to him. She touched the horse and said, "The poor, tired animal."

The man carried the bundles of wood under the shed to the woodpile. When he came back he answered mother. "He is not poorer and not more tired than I am, madam. The Lord knows it." After that I pitied a poor peasant almost as much as his horse.

Mother had the man put the horse in the stable—we had no horses at the time—and asked him to come into the house. "You will find some oats in a bin," she told him.

Mother gave the peasant a glass of spirits, a large piece of bread, and a plateful of warm lentils with pieces of smoked bacon in it.

"This is oats for me, good lady, as I may say with your leave," the man said. He sat down and ate heartily.

When he left I asked mother why the man called the lentils "oats." She explained that oats was the best feed for the horse, and the man made the comparison in praise of the lentils.

That evening we had boiled beef for dinner, one of my favorite dishes. I said, "Mother, this is oats for me." Mother laughed, but father looked at me in that peculiar, quizzical way of his, with one eyebrow raised and said, "What manner of talking is this?"

Mother told him the story and then he laughed too. We all laughed. After that, all kinds of food that father relished was oats for him also, until mother got tired of hearing it and made us stop.

Mother was very indulgent with us. For long periods

of time she would allow me or Irina to follow some child-
ish notion, like walking backward, which I liked to do,
especially when she watched me. Several times I fell and
once I hurt my head on the kitchen floor.

Mother did not scold, nor did she run to me solici-
tously and pick me up. She sat by the window sewing. She
had seen me start my backward march, then turned to her
work, and when she heard the thud my fall made, looked
up. All she said was, when I started to whimper, "You fell,
my little soul, now get up."

Of course I had hurt my head but dared not say it for
then I would have to give up walking backward. Mother
knew that my fall had been painful but she did not try to
soothe me.

Much later I learned that she wanted us to learn by
ourselves certain small lessons through experience.

But when she saw that it all was lasting too long, she
would suddenly put a definite stop to our "nonsense."

Bad habits often grow from innocent beginnings, she
said. And I wondered if mother had any bad habits. I
wondered if her never tiring of the one bedspread which
I did not like could be a bad habit.

This was an enormous bedspread with a full-length
portrait of Carmen Sylva, the Queen of Romania, woven
into the pattern. She sat spinning, the everlasting smile on
her motherly face. She had distaff and spindle just like the
peasant women used. Mother was very fond of that bedspread, because she admired and loved the unfortunate
queen who had lost her only child, a daughter, and was
unhappy with her Prussian husband, King Carol I. Then
one day father read us the poem she wrote, a mother's
heart-rending sorrow expressed in the magic of words.

220

Mother wept and Irina and I cried bitterly too, and the winter wind moaned outside. After that I did not dislike the bedspread so much. That was the first sweetly sad evening of my life. The next sad evening was when father read us the wonderful poem by Alexandri, titled *Pohod Na Sibir, Journey to Siberia.* A long column of people, condemned to exile in Siberia's vast desert, trudges painfully on snow-covered, wind-swept land toward a goal which many of the miserable lot never reaches. They fell and were left behind, a prey to the wolves howling on the low, gray horizon. When one of the unfortunates, whom the whip of the Cossack could no longer goad to move, dropped on the frozen snow, the Cossack would mark his passing out of misery on the handle of his whip. That was the tally on which the number of the dead was recorded. *Pohod Na Sibir.* This was the first poem I learned by heart, at the age of five.

With a long woolen shawl wound twice round my neck, the two ends covering my chest under the heavy, cumbersome winter coat, and high boots on my feet, mother sent me out to play in the yard. Irina had gone to school and so had all the children of seven and over. I felt lonesome. Besides, I envied my sister who could read the poems that father read to me and that I learned by heart.

So I decided to go to school. I opened the small gate that was cut in the large two-winged gate of the yard, and walked out into the deserted street. The sun on the snow made me blink against the sharp darts of light from the myriads of snow crystals. But the freedom of the empty street made me happy. I was out on a great adventure.

The snow-covered street seemed new to me, part of a new world into which I bravely set out toward a goal that made my heart thump. Mother used to say that knowledge was a priceless treasure and now I was on my way to find it.

I imagined myself in possession of all the knowledge in the world, astounding with it Uncle Gherasim and then the emperors and kings of all the countries on earth. They would send for me gorgeous carriages drawn by twenty white horses and mother would let me go, saying, "Farewell, my dear little soul, and come back soon safely." I would travel from one end of the world to the other, stopping in great cities where the multitude of people would greet me, welcome me to remain longer as their guest. I would thank them politely and say that I was on my way to such a king or emperor and could not tarry. Then the great crowds would cheer and follow me to the outskirts of the city and there bid me farewell in thousands of voices.

The emperors and kings would give me priceless gifts which I would bring home to my parents and to Irina. I would also give some of them to Ileana, to Uncle Gherasim, to Andronic, and a golden cross to Popa Radu. But the magic horse which I should find in the stables of an emperor—one that only I would recognize to be such, for he would look old and useless to everybody and the emperor would say, "If you care to have such a horse have him, Peter,"—this I would keep for myself.

On that horse I should travel ever afterward, "fast as thought," like the magic horses in Uncle Gherasim's stories.

With these fancies in my mind I walked along and very soon found myself in front of the school.

The schoolhouse was set back in a fence-enclosed yard. The gate was open. A wide path bordered by snow as high as my ears led to the door, two steps above the ground. I managed to open the door—my hands were very cold—and found myself in a hallway that seemed colder than the street.

The hum of voices flowed languidly in the cold, dark hallway. It reminded me of the mill canal where the deep water ran very smoothly and the huge winged water wheels were turning with a deep humming sound.

On tiptoe I walked to the first door on the right and knocked. There was no answer of "come in," so very quietly I opened it. Warm, stale air met me. The teacher, Vlad, did not see me, but all the eyes of the children were upon me. Slowly the teacher turned his head. Then he tapped his desk with the cane and ordered the children to look at their books and not let their eyes wander idly.

"What is it?" he asked me.

"I came to school," I said.

"Have your parents sent you?"

"No! I came to learn."

"Come here, Peter. What do you want to learn?"

"To read the poems in the calendar, like my sister, and get knowledge."

"Have you a slate and a book of A.B.C.'s?"

"If you will give them to me, father will pay."

At this point someone tittered. The teacher struck the desk sharply and said, "Silence." I looked and saw Irina cover her mouth with her hand.

The teacher came down from the platform where his desk and chair stood and helped me to take off my coat. I unwrapped the shawl myself.

"Sit here, Peter," the teacher said, indicating the first bench, where twelve or fourteen small boys sat. The girls

223

were on another bench at the left of the aisle. I sat down and my schooling started then and there.

At the noon recess, Irina made fun of me. "You are sitting on the first bench, that's where the dunces are," she said. And she would not walk home with me. I felt ashamed and cried. Mena, the loveliest girl in the school, took my hand and walked me home. My misery turned to gladness. There was rivalry between Mena and my sister. Irina was actually jealous of Mena and she tried to surpass her in school, but never quite succeeded, for Mena was very bright and self-possessed. And she was strong and very quick, which she proved that very afternoon when the children played in the schoolyard and Irina tried to throw her in the deep snow; it was herself who got thrown and I laughed. I paid for it when the bell called us in. Irina pulled my hair and pinched my arm. But I had another triumph that day. I asked the teacher to remove me from the dunces' bench and he gave me a seat in the second row. Then also, father praised me at dinnertime for having gone to school all by myself, although mother asked twice, "Is he not too small?" and looked at me as if I were having a colic.

A memorable winter, that. I had ventured out into a new world, the world of learning. And that winter I saw a dead person for the first time, old Anghelina whom everybody loved and respected. She had been the midwife for years and years and had great knowledge of the herbs with healing virtues.

Anghelina, dead, laid out in her best holiday clothes, with her hands folded over her chest, looked serene, peacefully asleep. Two candles burned at her head casting a flickering light on the old, pale face. Had Anghelina lived another month she would have reached the age of ninety. But Anghelina had told her friends that she had heard Archangel Gabriel calling her. "Twice the angel called me. When he calls the third time, I shall go," she had said.

Nobody knew whether Anghelina heard the last call, for she was found dead in bed one morning. Her crony, old Suzanna, had been with her the previous night. "A pleasant evening we spent together, chattering like two old magpies," Suzanna said.

Anghelina had been as generous in helping the sick as she was in teaching her knowledge of home remedies and of the medicinal virtues of herbs and roots to those who would hear it. And old Suzanna was the one who inherited from her lifelong friend most of this knowledge. She also inherited all the herbs that Anghelina had in store. But what Anghelina took with her into the beyond was a sweetness of nature and a kindly wisdom which were also healing virtues.

"Anghelina is living her days in the presence of God," the people used to say.

I looked at Anghelina's face with the child's disbelief in death, expecting to see her open her eyes at any instant and smile, as she used to smile when she came to us. Mother was holding my hand. Then I felt a tremor in her hand and looking up at her saw she was weeping. Suddenly I began to cry too. When mother wiped my tears she smiled and said, "Dear little soul, say 'God rest Baba Anghelina's soul in peace.'" I repeated the words and we left.

I asked mother why did Anghelina die. The word that had meant nothing to me now took on a significance because it concerned the old woman of whom everybody spoke with affection.

"She was old, my little soul, and her day had come," mother said.

"Suzanna is old, too," I said.

"Everybody who lives as long as Suzanna will grow old," mother said. That I could not understand at all. Old people were old, always, from the beginning. For me, at that age, everything was stationary, like the trees, the garden, the brook, and the hills with the vineyards. Death and old age were names, words that applied to women like Suzanna and men like Uncle Gherasim, and now to Anghelina the word death applied, but to her alone. I knew of course that the chickens we ate were killed, and so were the pigs killed in the autumn, so that we had a supply of sausages, meat, and bacon, but that had nothing to do with death.

CHAPTER 23

✿✿✿✿✿✿✿✿✿✿✿✿

WHEN THE PIGS WERE SLAUGHTERED, MOTHER CLOSED
herself in the small room farthest from the yard and
stuffed her ears, so as not to hear the terrible squealing of
the animals. Irina stuck her head under a pillow as she
did during thunderstorms. I merely stuck a finger in each
ear, standing at the kitchen window with my back to it, so
as not to see what was going on in the yard. On the hearth
the water in the large kettle was bubbling. But when the
bristles were being burned off the carcasses with burning straw, I ran out to watch the fire. The boiling water
was then carried out by Nicodin and spilled over the
animals sprawled out on boards. Vintila, the expert at
slaughtering, would then scrub the pigs with a brick and
boiling water, at which work Nicodin helped. When this
was done the hogs looked very clean and frightfully
naked.

Father had many accomplishments, one of which was
making sausages and a ragout of fresh pork. On the evening when the pigs were slaughtered, our house was an
anthill of activity. Father, in his shirt sleeves, his arms

227

bare to above the elbows, officiated in the kitchen, his face red as a ripe tomato. He moved about and gave orders with the air of a commanding officer. This was the only time when he could lord it over the kitchen and he took full advantage. Mother and the women who always came to help on these occasions smiled behind his back, approval on mother's face and amusement on the women's.

The ragout was cooked in a large iron kettle over a very strong fire on the hearth. The kettle stood on a high tripod under which the fire burned, and father attended to stirring the meat with a long wooden spoon. Then the big kitchen table had to be cleared and set for everybody; on this day there was absolute equality in our household between the family and the help. We all sat at the table, together with Nicodin, Anica the servant girl, Vintila the expert, and the women who helped, plus Popa Radu the priest, and his wife, "Priestess Porfira" as the peasants called her.

We went to bed, Irina and I, to the sound of a rat-at-tat-ta, produced by the helpers chopping the meat for the sausages. It was a pleasant, homey sound which, since we were already drowsy from the activities of the day and the ragout, put us to sleep as soon as we were in bed.

When in the morning I went into the kitchen, the embers on the hearth were still glowing from the fire that had lasted way past midnight. But the surprise was the yards of sausage hanging over a long pole suspended from the ceiling and covered with a linen cloth.

Mother rose late, father still later, and Irina and I had the kitchen to ourselves. Anica let us do anything we liked, except touch the sausages.

The warm air in the kitchen was heavy with the smell of

228

garlic, pepper, and other spices. This smell I always associate with those important occasions, which ushered in the winter. For, when the pigs were slaughtered, the cabbage was already seasoning in brine, and all the other vegetables providing us during the long stretch of winter with wholesome food were stored away. After the pigs were slaughtered winter could come. In fact, as the peasants used to say, winter was already knocking on the door.

Indeed, winter was coming, for a few days later I woke up one morning and the room was full of that subdued light that snow gives as it falls quietly and lies on the ground, on the roofs, and on trees. The flakes glided down on the windowpanes and lay gently on the outer sill already covered with soft snow. On that morning the family greeting was "Winter's here, good morning," which we gave to one another and to winter too. And we all felt happy and closer to each other than ever, and the home was an island of safety against this friend which knew no other rule in the game it played with human beings but that of its own nature. To many people its ways were harsh, even cruel, but to me they were friendly and cheering.

During the Christmas holidays of the memorable year when I started going to school we had a visitor from Bucharest, an old friend of father's, a very learned man who, among several languages, knew English also. He was an ethnographer, a student of folkways, and expert in Romanian peasant art and lore. He was a tall, lean man with black hair and gray eyes like father's, which not merely smiled but seemed to dance when a smile appeared on his face and grew slowly like a day of spring. His name was Andrei Cioban. Father did not call him by his first name, but by a nickname he got as a child, Ciobanel, which means little shepherd, since Cioban stands for shepherd. So, we children called him Uncle Ciobanel.

He was very fond of father and even more fond of mother, whom he called Vara, diminutive of Barbara, or Varvara in Romanian. Vara stands for summer, too.

"And how is my dear Vara in the dead of winter?" was his greeting to mother. Uncle Ciobanel brought presents for all of us. Irina and mother's gifts were beautiful sheepskin vests, elaborately embroidered; to father and me he brought Persian-lamb caps. Fortunately Uncle Ciobanel knew what a large head was mine, so there was little difference between the sizes of the two caps, excepting that father's was higher.

Mother was always uneasy when Uncle Ciobanel came to us, for he usually stayed a week or more, which could give father ample time to start a discussion on some political question. Father had very definite views on politics and he defended them passionately against all contrary views, no matter whose they were. When father launched out on those waters Uncle Ciobanel would quietly remain on his safe shore, smiling good-naturedly and bidding father safe journey.

One evening father came home all agitated, holding the paper rolled up so it looked like a small club. He struck the table with it and shouted, "Scoundrels, the devil's unchristened idiots."

Uncle Ciobanel, standing by the window, smiled but said nothing. Mother was sitting on the edge of her favorite chair, ready to rise and pacify father, who glared at

230

his smiling friend. Then he said, "You, who have a mind—supposedly—all of you, who live in books and musty things of the past, you let the politicians take the country to the devil. Are you never to wake up?"

"We have learned some things, Pavel, but so far as the mind is concerned, if we have any at all, it is just enough for our work. It is men like you, Pavel, who have more mind than you need for your occupation, who must take care of these other matters," Uncle Ciobanel said.

"Go to the devil, you Jesuit," father said, and he turned sharply to mother. He suspected that mother and Uncle Ciobanel were agreed that he was wasting his ability as district notary, when he could practice law in one of the large cities, as mother wanted him to do. But he said nothing to mother. He merely stood there looking at her.

Mother said, "You really must get yourself another scarf, dear. And take off your coat."

"Upf," father exclaimed, swung around, and threw off his coat and scarf. Then he picked up the scarf, examined it and said, "Shall I give it to Ciobanel for his collection?" He threw it to Uncle Ciobanel. "Look, expert. See if it is old enough for you." Uncle Ciobanel caught the long piece of woolen cloth deftly, turned to the window with it, and after a few moments said, "It's aged with wear, but not years. Still, I will have it for my collection. Shall I label it 'Hybrid art, woven by Saxons, pure *Tzigaia* wool. Worn by Pavel Roman until the year of our Lord 1899, and generously donated to the Ethnographic Museum'?"

"Go to the devil," father said, but his anger was gone. When at dinner he tried to bring up the subject of the politicians, Uncle Ciobanel having started a discussion with mother about old home remedies, said, "Allow me, Pavel, I must get some details from Vara on herbs she has mentioned to me."

Father pushed out his mustaches and made a grimace, but said nothing. During the meal, mother and Uncle Ciobanel carried on their conversation about herbs and incantations, while father simply grunted now and again, and made faces like a man who was tasting bitter fruit.

Uncle Ciobanel was really a learned man. Father conceded this and was proud of him, for they were childhood friends. But he had two grievous faults—he would not discuss politics, and he never married.

During Uncle Ciobanel's visit father said to him one evening at the dinner table, "Now really, Ciobanel, why the devil don't you get married?"

"Because Vara never had a sister, one just like herself," Uncle Ciobanel said. Mother laughed a little but she blushed. Mother often blushed.

"Look at her," father said. "Gullible woman! He likes your cooking, my dear, that is what he means."

"I did not blush," mother said, but she touched her cheeks with the back of her hand.

"Blessed are those who can blush for they are pure in heart," Uncle Ciobanel said. He looked at mother adoringly.

"I think I shall have to put him out of the house," father mumbled as if to himself. Then, as I was imagining father putting Uncle Ciobanel out into the night in the cold, they all started to laugh. When mother laughed so heartily she always had to wipe the tears from her eyes. Because they laughed so, we too, Irina and I, began to laugh. But as we had finished our meal, we could ask permission to leave the table. We kissed mother and father and thanked them for the dinner, then we let Uncle Ciobanel kiss us on both cheeks. When we went to bed we were still laughing and never knew why.

Uncle Ciobanel stayed out the week without father succeeding in getting him into a discussion on politics. After he left, father said to mother, "I like Ciobanel, but really Vara, he is a mole."

"But dear, he has good eyes, and moles—they have no eyes at all," mother said.

"Oh, well, you can't understand," father said. As he walked out he added, "or you will not."

Mother resumed her sewing, smiling to herself.

᭢᭢᭢᭢᭢᭢᭢᭢᭢᭢᭢᭢

CHAPTER 24

ON SUNDAYS FATHER WOULD READ THE BIBLE TO us and, when our attention lagged, he would retell us the story, much embellished with inventions of his own. These readings took place before church in the early morning, and we had to attend them washed and dressed, so we had to rise "with night on our heads," as the peasants say.

Father had a deep, pleasant voice and my sister's face, shiny clean, smelled like a rose because on Sundays mother washed her with rose-scented glycerine soap.

When we heard the story of Adam and Eve for the first time, Irina asked, "Father, what is Paradise like?" I felt annoyed by her question because I had an imaginary picture in my mind of Paradise. But father's answer cheered me. He said, "Paradise is like our village."

Certainly, I thought, how could it be different? Can there be lovelier fields, trees more beautiful, and happier songbirds than ours in Paradise? And what would Paradise be without father and mother and Irina—although I always wished she were not left-handed.

The tree of knowledge of good and evil was in our garden, a very big walnut tree. And Irina was Eve, I Adam. That was why I never took one single nut from her, but always said, "Give me two, Irina."

"Why do you always want two nuts?" she asked and finally I told her. "Because I don't want to be tempted by the fruit from the tree of knowledge of good and evil."

"But that was an apple tree, silly, and Eve took a bite from the apple first; you can't bite into a walnut," she said and laughed. She also taunted me saying there was no serpent coiled round the tree like in the "true pictures" she saw in our Bible story book.

Really, Irina often invaded my imaginary world with her "reality." She learned the word from our teacher, Simeon Vlad, who came one evening a week to have dinner with us and talk worldly affairs with father. I remember when she asked him, "Please, domnule Vlad, what is reality?"

Vlad looked a little taken aback, I thought, for he glanced at father, who said, "Tell her."

"Reality is what you can see, taste, smell, touch, and hear," he said, and Irina thanked him. Then, when no one saw her, she turned to me and stuck out her tongue. In return I pushed the tip of my nose up. She had a pug nose.

Oh! But when Uncle Gherasim told us stories, with dragons, fairy queens, goblins and furies and other creatures as fantastic, Irina sat spellbound, forgetting reality entirely.

Uncle Gherasim was old, as old as winter I thought, because there was a picture of winter in the calendar. His beard was not white, only gray, but winter is not always all white either.

Perhaps too, I associated Uncle Gherasim with winter because it was in the winter he told us his wonderful stories. In the other seasons he was too busy all day and when night fell he went to bed. And he told us that as soon as spring came he put away his stories and never brought them out until winter.

Irina was bold enough to ask him where he put his stories, and Uncle Gherasim said, "I put them in the chest called silence, which nobody can open but me."

Uncle Gherasim was fond of all of us, father included, but he loved mother with all his generous heart, and called her Mandra, which means "beautiful" and also "sweetheart."

Mother always welcomed him joyfully to our home. Often they spoke together earnestly about Irina and me. But he never called me "my little soul." That was my mother's privilege.

Mother was always cheerful, except on the days when she noticed a stain on her index finger and thumb. She called these "candle-flame stains." On such days mother would fall into melancholy meditation, and spend long periods of time looking at photographs of my uncles—her brothers—whom she had not seen in two or three years because father had quarreled with them over political questions.

The occasions were rare when mother observed those stains, which could have been caused by her holding a carrot in her fingers when cleaning it, or even from lighting a sulphur match and holding it too close to the igniting end. Such occasions did occur, however, and then our home became wrapped in gray sadness.

Fortunately the periods did not last long, unless father happened to be absent from home for a whole day.

Father made light of mother's interpretation of these stains, saying that if all messengers of ill tidings could so readily be disposed of with mere soap and rubbing, life would be a song. And he suspected that mother made no sufficient effort to get rid of them. Sometimes, though rarely, he lost his temper when mother insisted that these signs would last out their own time no matter how she tried to wash them away, because they indicated the death of someone near to her.

"I will rub them off," father said one time, but mother hid her hand under her left armpit and would not let him touch it.

Father grumbled and groaned, then he said, "Barbara, I am amazed. You have more silly notions and beliefs than the peasants. Herbs, incantations, bites by a twin, and God knows what more, and now these smudges on your fingers."

Mother smiled sweetly as she always did when she felt in the right. She said, "Dear, you are so very intelligent and full of knowledge and yet you close your eyes to things, and then you say they do not exist. Are the herbs bad? And how about the pot covers? Are they not the best remedy for aches in the stomach? And the peasants are not silly. Their beliefs are not silly. When Dr. Bran could not help you—and you had faith in him—a peasant woman brought us herbs that cured you of stones in the bladder. You believed in Dr. Bran's knowledge, but it was the herbs that helped you. So, dear, *your* belief was wrong."

Father was a little nonplussed but he recovered soon and said, "It is these silly stains on your fingers I was talking about, Barbara."

"Dear, how can you say that? You spoke about the silly notions and beliefs of the peasants. These good people to whom you are sacrificing your career," mother said.

"O God!" father exclaimed and he left the room. He knew that from that point onward he would lose every argument against mother's beliefs. She would stick to that one statement like a tick; he was sacrificing a brilliant career by remaining as notary in the village. He could practice law in the city, like his friends Timotei and De Lemeny. Was he not a better lawyer than they? Did they not come and consult him? What could he say against such arguments?

He might have told mother, of course, that he could do more good for the people where he was. That he loved the village and he loved his kind of life. That his working in the garden from early spring until the middle of autumn gave him vigor, kept him in excellent health. And cutting wood in winter for an hour or two was the most health-giving exercise. He might have told all this to mother—but would that be a strong enough argument against her? Not at all!

No! Because mother simply would have smiled sweetly and said, "You see, dear, you like this peasant life. You believe in this way of living more than in the way of city life. So?" And again she would win. Therefore, father could only exclaim, "O God!" and run off. The truth is that father was attached to the peasants, wanted to help them as much as he could, and he loved the land. Better to say, he loved the earth. The peasants call the earth "our mother," and father often used this phrase. And he was a wizard at raising vegetables. The garden was his paradise. Men like Uncle Gherasim and Andronic, the wheelwright, he said, were peers of any of the best among men. Andronic was a master at his craft and he was a marvelous bone-setter. When father broke his leg it was Andronic who took care of it, not Dr. Bran. And later, when father's prize riding horse broke its leg, Andronic set the fracture and made the sling that kept the horse off his broken leg.

As to Uncle Gherasim, he was, father said, "a good man all through." I remember when Uncle Gherasim said to father, "People are good until they find something that spoils them. Then is the time they need help and he who can must give it."

Mother asked, "What must we do, Uncle Gherasim, to remain good?"

"Just never turn away from the face of God," Uncle Gherasim said.

Uncle Gherasim was very kind, but he was a lion at fighting against any wrong. Minor matters of wrong he treated most simply. He was not a man to fan a spark into conflagration, as father used to say. It happened once that Pavel Gorun, whose land touched Uncle Gherasim's, took three furrows from Uncle Gherasim's land. When Uncle Gherasim came out to plow his parcel, Pavel was there.

Uncle Gherasim said to him, "Well, Pavel, did you mean to plow up my land too?"

239

Pavel straightened up and stopped the oxen. "How so?" he asked.

"You went three furrows into my land," Uncle Gherasim said.

"Not at all! My land goes that far," Pavel said.

"The two stones that mark the border, you have not seen them?" Uncle Gherasim asked.

"Maybe the stones were moved," Pavel said rather angrily.

"Pavel, the stones were not moved, but if you hold they were, the register in the notary's office will tell the size of our fields. Shall we go to the notary?" Uncle Gherasim said.

Pavel said not a word in answer. He called to the oxen and continued with his plowing. He went the length of the field and came back, calling to the oxen louder than he needed. When he got to the end of the field he shouted to Uncle Gherasim, "Maybe I did cut one furrow into your field, but not more. I stand by that."

"You cut three furrows, Pavel," Uncle Gherasim said calmly.

Pavel was a quick-tempered man, but he was honest. "One furrow, that I admit. Not a finger's breadth more. Take it or go to the devil."

Uncle Gherasim made no answer. He went and found the stones, then set to plowing his field. He knew the stones could not have been moved. They were set deep in the ground and too heavy for five men to move if they were above ground.

When the season for cutting the wheat came, Uncle Gherasim left the wheat standing on the breadth of the three furrows. The men helping him said, "But, the markers are farther. This wheat is yours."

"No! It is not mine. Pavel plowed the land, he put in the seed, the wheat is his," Uncle Gherasim said.

Several days later Pavel came to Uncle Gherasim. "I came to speak to you," he said.

"Speak, Pavel," Uncle Gherasim replied.

"About that matter of the three furrows. The men said they saw the markers between our fields. I am no thief."

"I did not say you were, Pavel."

"How are we to settle the matter then?" Pavel asked.

"I left the wheat standing. You saw it."

"I did see it, but what shall I do? Leave it there for the birds and field mice?" Pavel asked.

"No, cut it, Pavel, it is yours. But for next year, keep to the line which marks our fields."

Pavel cut the wheat. He kept the harvest from the three furrows separately. After threshing he brought half of the wheat to Uncle Gherasim.

"I can't accept it, Pavel. You made a mistake about the line. So I believe," Uncle Gherasim said.

"I did see the stones," Pavel said contritely.

"But you thought they might have been moved."

"I did. A little, not altogether," Pavel said.

"Well, you believed a little. You plowed and seeded down the soil. So, take the wheat and go in peace."

Pavel swung the sack onto his shoulder. "Forgive me, Uncle Gherasim," he said. He walked slowly out of the yard.

Everybody praised Uncle Gherasim. Pavel had to defend himself. "I offered to make good. Uncle Gherasim knows I made a mistake. Ask him."

There was not one person of Uncle Gherasim's generation who could read or write. In his time, he told mother, the priest had the burden of teaching children this art. The priest was willing enough, but he had no pupils. Peasant children must be an asset in the household or they become a liability. And, Uncle Gherasim added, it happens that the poorer people have the most children. So, a girl of six can rock the cradle, bring in wood for the hearth, or tend the goat at pasture. Boys of that age can do many little chores, too, so they are kept at home.

And in those days, Uncle Gherasim said, there was no compulsory education. The city folk and the officials were sure that for a peasant schooling was unnecessary, if not actually a waste of time.

Uncle Gherasim was eighteen years old when he went to the priest one Sunday and begged to be taught "the letters, to read and to write them," as he put it. The priest was glad to have a pupil, "even though I was a full-grown man already," Uncle Gherasim said. "So during the Sundays of one autumn, and one winter, I learned to read and write. I felt like a man who has found a treasure. I made my father pay half of the subscription for the newspaper with our priest. We got the paper the same day it came, after his reverence read it. When I got so I could read almost as well as I could talk, my joy was great. I felt as if I were looking at the whole world and hearing it, right from our home."

Mother said it was wonderful of him to have done what he had, and smiled at me, for it was in the same winter I started going to school. During that winter and the following spring I, too, learned to read and write all the letters in the alphabet and also to read short sentences in the calendar, and to write them.

It was an eventful winter, that. We got a new priest in our village, as Popa Nicolai was too old to be a "shepherd of the Lord," as the peasants call their priest. And mother performed something close to a miracle that very winter.

Mother was not stubborn. She simply held onto her beliefs, smiling at father's efforts to convince her otherwise. And she would listen to him and not say a word.

"But I am right, am I not?" father would say in a sort of masculine desperation. At this point mother would go over, kiss him, and smilingly say, "Yes, my dear husband."

What amazed Irina and me was that father kept trying.

One of mother's beliefs was that pain was something that had to last out its term, like a lease. She scorned medicine, but had unshakable faith in every kind of home remedy. She had in store a variety of herbs, in linen bags, which were not marked in any way, for she knew them all by the scent.

If any one of us got a cold, there was the elderberry blossom tea and the tea from dried raspberries, which had to be taken very hot and in large quantities. For headaches, a cloth soaked in cold water and vinegar tied over the forehead was all the remedy. The fact that the headache would persist for several hours was in the nature of the pain, which had to go its full term. It was true, however, that the cold water and vinegar gave a little relief.

We were a healthy lot, but we did get an occasional bellyache. And this was nothing at all in mother's estimation, nor was this kind of discomfort, as she called it, restricted to us children. Father would get it sometimes and mother, too. The remedy for this was simplicity itself.

We had an assortment of earthen pots of various sizes, and each had a cover to match, also earthen. When one of us was suffering with a bellyache, a pot cover, the size of the person's abdomen, would be heated, wrapped in a piece of linen, and applied. Father needed the largest pot cover, myself the smallest.

Mother was a great hand at preserving. Our cellar was stocked with all sorts of fruit preserves. Vegetables such as celery knobs, carrots, parsnips, and turnips we kept in sand on the cellar floor. String beans and ripe tomatoes she kept in linen bags in the attic, the driest place in the house, after they had been dried in the oven.

The cabbage is one of the staple foods with the peasants, on a par with the potato and the bean. From midsummer, when the first cabbages began to form heads, until spring, the cabbage appeared in one form or another on the peasant's table.

We had a huge vat, in which mother would store a hundred heads of cabbage in brine. This was an art with her. The juice of this cabbage had great medicinal virtues. Principally, it is a marvelous laxative and good to taste, especially the way mother seasoned it. She put in the brine sour cherry leaves, dill, tarragon, horseradish roots, a little garlic, and a few pungent red peppers. She also had some red cabbages in the vat and these colored the cabbage juice.

We knew the virtues of this juice and so mother did a good turn to the young priest, Popa Vasile Dumbravean. He came to our village to replace Popa Radu temporarily, who had to go to his brother where there was illness and lengthy litigations concerning some property in which he had an interest. A tall, thin man he was, pale as potato sprouts, but his black eyes had a fire in them.

On their first visit to us, mother took the young wife aside and led the conversation to the young priest. He was too pale, mother thought, for a young man and especially for a village priest. The peasants like to see their priest vigorous and rosy.

Mother found out the trouble. Since his days in the seminary the poor fellow had suffered.

When Popa Vasile and his wife left, the young woman carried a large jug of our cabbage juice, covered with a white linen napkin.

A few days later she came to report to mother the amazing results of the wonderful remedy. And she asked to have another jugful of it.

Popa Vasile Dumbravean was getting some color in his face and that fire in his eyes had almost disappeared, together with his frown. Then came Lent, six weeks of it, before Easter. For that period the usual fare for the believers is beans, lentils, salt fish once or twice a week, potatoes, onions, and radishes with linseed or pumpkinseed oil. Naturally, a priest must observe the fast days most strictly.

So it happened that in the last week of Lent Popa Vasile Dumbravean consumed a large quantity of our cabbage juice. He became a new man by Easter. "Thank God, and thank you, doamna Roman, my husband is a strong, healthy man now," his wife said.

CHAPTER 25

⊙⊙⊙⊙⊙⊙⊙⊙⊙⊙⊙⊙

MOTHER WAS VERY PIOUS. WHEN IN THE STREET SHE heard some peasant curse she stuffed up her ears and whispered, "God forgive him, the poor man does not know what he is saying." She believed that her prayer would win the Lord's grace for the sinner.

In our home the word "devil" was strictly forbidden. Father would say the word because his temper would get the better of him, but mother always glanced at him reproachingly. So the next time he would say *"the black one"* and with a triumphant look in his eyes say to mother, "But you know what I mean."

The Romanian word for devil is *dracul.* This word had a great fascination for me, especially since I had no difficulty with the letter *r*, like teacher Vlad's wife, who said Maliana instead of Mariana. Yet I never dared repeat the word. I would say quietly, when alone, dra, dra, several times, tempted most terribly to add the rest of the letters. Then one day the thing happened.

Irina pushed me into a snowbank. I fell and scratched my nose and forehead. I was very angry. The scratches

246

hurt sharply and were bleeding. Irina got scared. She wanted to wipe off the blood with her handkerchief. I pushed her away shouting, *"Dute dracului*—Go to the devil!"* I said it with such a relish that the pain stopped entirely. But I paid for it. All that winter long Irina kept me in bondage. I had to obey her like a slave or she would tell mother. My sister was a tyrant really. Even mother had said once to Uncle Gherasim in desperation that she wondered whom Irina could resemble. Once, when she had a cold in the head and spoke through her nose in the funniest way, mother brewed elderberry blossom tea for her. Irina would not drink it. Then she would have to drink raspberry tea, mother said. Pouting, Irina nodded yes. But when Anica, our servant girl, brought it to her she pushed the cup away. And she would not drink the cabbage juice either, which after all was absolutely required in cases of colds. So she was punished. She could not have pancakes with plum jelly which she liked as much as she liked the honey Uncle Gherasim brought us. But she still held the threat over me; and she made me steal, yes, actually steal, one pancake from the kitchen and bring it to her. But I was sure that Anica saw me and that consoled me a little about the grievous sin of stealing.

"Did anybody see what you did?" Irina asked me, grinning. "No!" I answered sharply. Lying to Irina in these cases was absolutely no sin, I thought.

My uncles on mother's side were all men of learning. Uncle Alexander, the oldest, was a physician, Uncle Paul was a professor of mathematics, and the other two, Andrei and Stefan, were in the clergy.

Uncle Stefan was the youngest. He was of medium

height, had very broad shoulders and a deep chest; a studious man, like his brothers, yet very jovial and fond of good living. What an eye he had for good-looking girls.

When he came to visit us in the village, in no time at all he spotted the most beautiful peasant girl, even if she happened to be in bare feet, coming from the marshes where the hemp was thawing, her legs up to her knees black with marsh mud.

And in no time at all he would know the girl's name, the name of her parents and of her relatives, too. He had an astonishing memory to boot.

Father never quarreled with Uncle Stefan because they never discussed politics together. The first time father brought up such a topic Uncle Stefan told him, laughing, that he was giving his life to serve man through religion and the church, and he was a perfect ignoramus in political matters. Naturally father would not waste time with an ignoramus. Politics was, in fact, something the priests should keep their noses out of, he said. Uncle Stefan agreed cheerfully; he knew what had happened between his brother Andrei and father. And, if the truth be told, between his other two brothers and father.

Uncle Stefan used to tell mother that only happy people have favor before God. To be happy, he said, was a testimony to God that He had created a good world.

Mother laughed heartily at his humorous stories, and when he got to talking about the prophets and the Bible she clasped her hands in wonderment and admiration at his understanding of the holy scriptures. She looked at him earnestly, drinking in his words, to say when he stopped speaking, "Stefan, how beautiful it is, but I can't understand it at all."

248

Uncle Andrei had told us that Uncle Stefan had gone into metaphysical regions, dragging the Holy Book into a field that was beyond the borders of the clergy's ken.

"He is jeopardizing his career, with a mind like his, too. He would go far if not for this twist in his mind. But Barbara, do not worry, he is young. In time he will realize that his searching beneath the surface—as he says—is nothing but the flames of youth. He will get married and open his eyes to see that the hierarchy of our priesthood knows the word of the Lord well enough to guide the believers on the right path."

"It must be as you say," mother answered, although all she got from Uncle Andrei's talk was that married life would open Uncle Stefan's eyes.

Everybody loved Uncle Stefan. Even the bishop spoke well of him, despite the fact that he had reprimanded him several times for delving in Apocrypha.

Having been anointed, Uncle Stefan waited six months, then he was given a church in a village in our district. He took the place of Popa Nicolai Vlad, who, being past the age of eighty, retired from shepherding the Lord's sheep, to wait the call of Archangel Gabriel in peace.

We knew Popa Nicolai Vlad. He came to us several times to consult father on legal matters. He was a big man, with a large, red face, his long locks, beard, and mustaches snow white. He smelled of wine and incense, and ate with an appetite that won mother's admiration. His village numbered over four hundred families, which means a large village in which a priest can prosper. Popa Nicolai Vlad had prospered. He had had sixty years to prosper in by the time Uncle Stefan came to take his place.

If Uncle Stefan had been a Greek Orthodox priest he

would have had to get himself a wife before he could obtain a church, but as a Greek Catholic, he got the church first. That he considered fortunate.

"It gives me time to consider and to choose. A wife is not a church," he said.

One year passed and Uncle Stefan was still a bachelor priest. Mother started thinking. Then another year passed and mother began to worry.

"Do not torment yourself, Barbara, your brother can manage his life well enough. Besides, my dear, he is still young," father said.

"Young! He is twenty-four already," mother said. Then she added in a lowered voice, "He is very fond of women."

Father laughed, but said nothing. This annoyed mother. "Oh!" she exclaimed, rose from the table, and left the room. But soon she returned, came to father, and very earnestly asked, "Do you know Stefan better than I?"

"Well, dear Barbara, I don't know if I do, but you see, dear, I am a man," father said chuckling.

"Oh!" mother exclaimed again, then looking at us children she laughed and said, "Now children, go out and play."

In the garden I said to my sister, "Irina, I am a man, like father and Uncle Stefan."

"Ha-ha! A man," Irina said, and ran away, laughter trailing behind her.

In the third year Uncle Stefan married. And whom did he marry? A very poor girl, Alexandra, daughter of Paraschiva Moga, a widow in her middle thirties who still looked very young, mother said. "A young mother-in-law is nearer to the young generation," Uncle Stefan said and, he added, "Life is ever young."

250

We all went to the wedding. I was very happy and so was Irina, although she tried hard not to jump and clap her hands as I did. And I thought that Alexandra was the most beautiful girl in all the world.

At the wedding supper mother asked Uncle Stefan quietly, "Why did you wait so long to get married?"

"Because she was too young," Uncle Stefan said.

"There are scores of lovely girls here, Stefan," mother said.

"But only one Alexandra," Uncle Stefan said.

I blushed happily at his answer, but more so because Alexandra smoothed my forehead and said, "Eat another piece of honey cake, Peter, I baked it myself."

Never have I tasted better honey cake. And this second piece that Alexandra gave me tasted better than the first.

It must have been very late because while I watched everybody dance I fell asleep sitting on the bench by the wall, and woke up in the morning in a strange room. Soon mother came in.

"Where are we, mother?" I asked.

"We are at Mayor Simeon Vultur's. Come, get washed and dressed, then we will have breakfast and leave for home," mother said.

"Where are Uncle Stefan and Alexandra?" I asked.

"At their home, my darling," mother said.

"I want to say good-by to them, mother," I said.

"We will all say good-by to them, my little lamb," mother said.

Uncle Stefan and Alexandra came out in the yard to welcome us. They were holding hands. We went in the house but did not stay long. When taking leave mother said to Uncle Stefan, "I can see now why you waited. The

251

Lord bless you both with a long, happy life and with good children."

I heard mother, but I was looking at Alexandra. She had golden hair like the angels on the icons but she was more beautiful than any angel. This I did not tell Irina because I knew it was a sin to put Alexandra's beauty above that of the angels.

It began to be rumored in the district that Stefan was different from other priests. It was said he performed miracles. Not great miracles like raising the dead or healing the blind, but little miracles like bringing peace and harmony where there was strife, and moderating the ways of habitual drunkards. And he had a roomful of books and spent much time reading.

He was ever ready to respond to the call of anybody in distress. And his very presence brought relief. He sat at the bedside of the ailing person and spoke. He was not understood entirely but his words induced a soothing calm in the patient and in the rest of the people in the home.

We heard that the mayor's daughter, Maria Vultur, a girl of nineteen, had suddenly fallen ill and she could not sleep. She had fits of weeping from which nothing could save her. She wept bitterly until she fell exhausted into a heart-rending, feeble moaning. For nearly a week the girl suffered, despite the potions the old woman prepared and made her take. They called Uncle Stefan in the dead of night.

The mother took Uncle Stefan into the girl's room. She placed the candle on the table and left. The girl had wept all evening and now she was moaning feebly, her eyes wide open, focused on the ceiling. She held her hands pressed to her breasts and moaned.

"I listened, my ear glued against the closed door," the mother told neighbors. "For quite some time I heard nothing but Maria's moans. The priest spoke to her quietly for some time, and then she stopped suddenly. What the priest said to her we shall never know. Maria says only that the man is wonderful. Before he left the room, I heard him talking again to Maria, but so quietly I could not catch what he said. And he talked for a long time. She answered as quietly as he spoke. When I heard him coming toward the door I ran to the bench at the hearth. 'Maria is well, she will sleep,' he said, and walked out. I went to the gate with him. I took his hand to kiss—as we do to our priest—but he stopped me. He said, 'Humble yourself before the Lord only. We are one, all of us. The Lord bless you.'"

Now, it was known in the village that the mayor's daughter was being courted by the schoolteacher, Anton Vina, but she loved Pavel Coman, the blacksmith's son.

This Vina was the son of a priest and as schoolteacher a desirable son-in-law to the mayor. He was proud and kept himself aloof from the peasants, a manner for which neither the mayor nor his wife blamed him, because they, too, felt somewhat superior.

When he came to dinner, on Sundays, his hair was as shiny as Maria's Sunday boots, and he sat stiffly at the table. The pomade on his hair had a strong scent. Maria did not like the smell. He also used long words which he emphasized while looking at the faces around him. One virtue he had, however; he could blush, and blush he did when Maria would answer some of his tortuous questions simply and tersely.

The parents chided Maria each time the teacher left without her seeing him to the gate—which was every time.

Now, as to Pavel, the blacksmith's son. He was a different sort of a man altogether. He was a giant in stature and in strength, with the disposition of a happy child. To Pavel all seasons of the year were spring. "He gladdens one's heart," the people said, and the smithy was ever packed with children. They loved Pavel, were fascinated by his work and his singing. Pavel always sang, and the hammer was a tool of magic in his hand. When he put a glowing piece of iron on the anvil and plied his magic hammer, sparks flew and the hammer sang with Pavel. For he struck the iron and then let the hammer sing on the anvil, a pattering, metallic song. In no time the piece of iron would turn into a horseshoe or a huge spike, which Pavel, with a swing of his arm, would throw into the water trough hewn out of a large piece of timber. How he made this throw with the clumsy tongs was ever a wonder to the children.

Pavel was working at the anvil when Uncle Stefan came to see him a few days after he had seen the mayor's daughter. Pavel stopped singing and, smiling broadly, answered the priest's greeting. But his hammer did not stop.

"The iron would not wait, your reverence," he said after he threw the finished horseshoe into the trough.

"No, Pavel, it would not. It must be struck and shaped while it yields," the priest said.

Pavel nodded, showing his teeth in a smile. Simeon, Pavel's father, came into the smithy. He greeted the priest, walked to the forge, pushed the coals together, and then turned to face the visitor. He said, "Evening is falling, would your reverence do us the honor of coming into the house?"

"Thank you, I would if . . ." the priest said pointing to the forge where the coals were still glowing.

"Our work is done for today. With a little time in the morning we can easily catch up what might have remained over," Simeon said.

"You spoke about the iron not waiting," Uncle Stefan said to Pavel. They were sitting by the table.

"It is true, reverence," Pavel said with a short laugh.

"And when a girl loves a man she does not like to wait, Pavel," Uncle Stefan said.

Pavel blushed. "Your reverence knows about Maria and me?" he asked quietly.

"Yes, Pavel, I know. And I told her you will go and speak to her parents."

"Her parents want the teacher for a son-in-law," Pavel said earnestly.

"I spoke to them, too. Maria is their only child. They want her to be happy. I convinced them of that," Uncle Stefan said.

Pavel asked Uncle Stefan what to say to Maria's parents. Uncle Stefan told him not to worry about it. "The words will come to you when you are there," he said.

This was in the middle of the week. On Sunday Pavel went to Maria's. In the meantime Uncle Stefan had three visits with the schoolteacher.

We never learned what had passed between Uncle Stefan and the teacher at those meetings. All he told mother was that he ignited the spark of righteousness in the teacher's soul into a good flame.

"It needed fanning, that is true, but I had patience," he said.

Pavel and Maria were married that autumn. Uncle Stefan married them. He also persuaded the teacher to accept the invitation and come to the wedding.

Pavel and Maria christened their first child, a boy, Stefan, in homage to my uncle who had performed a miracle for them. In fact two miracles; curing Maria of her illness, and bringing about their marriage.

Of course Uncle Stefan would never be a bishop, his brothers said, because he was getting more and more absorbed in his metaphysical studies. But father said, "Stefan would never be happier with a purple sash across his middle and a golden cross on his chest, than he is as a miracle-working priest in a prosperous village."

Even mother, at length, agreed with him. "It is a great gift his," mother said.

"The greatest gift, Barbara, to be a man with a heart," father said, repeating the words of the peasants. Uncle Gherasim, who was present, said, "Amen."

CHAPTER 26

⊙⊙⊙⊙⊙⊙⊙⊙⊙⊙⊙⊙

MY PARENTS WERE NEVER AFRAID OF DISCUSSING family matters in the presence of Uncle Gherasim and Andronic, the wheelwright. They were very close to us.

While Uncle Gherasim liked to talk, Andronic liked rather to sit and listen. Not that he would not speak, but father said he weighed his words as carefully as a druggist weighs medicine. I wondered where Andronic kept the scales with which he weighed his words. But I was not like Irina who, had she wondered about it as I did, would have gone to him and asked, "Bade Andronic, where are the scales?"

My sister was a chatterbox. It is true that I envied her a little because she could speak so rapidly while I was slow of speech. If anybody asked me a question she would answer as if I were dumb. But I pronounced every word distinctly and teacher Vlad praised me for it. And I thought that possibly I, too, had a pair of scales in my head somewhere where my words got weighed like Andronic's.

When I reached so far in my book learning, as Nicodin

257

called it, that I could copy the poems from the calendar which I already knew by heart from father, I learned to read them too. Father taught me how the poems should be read. With my sister he had a struggle.

"But listen, daughter, how is it Peter can read them as they should be read—and you—you throw out the words rata-ta-ta-ta, like beans dropping on the floor? Now beans, Irina, beans are all alike, but words, dear, are not. Words are like money. Like coins. Here—this is copper. These are silver. One of the silver coins is smaller than the other and both are smaller than the copper coin. But the copper coin has less value than the smallest of the silver coins. Now, do you understand what I mean?"

"Yes, father," Irina said, pouting, and she threw me an angry look.

"Now, dear, read this over and remember, words are like money," father said. Irina started, a little slower at first, then it was again like beans dropping on the floor.

Father was red in the face. Drops of sweat appeared on his forehead. "I have the patience of a saint," he grumbled, and again started Irina from the beginning. Mother was sewing at the other end of the table. She looked up at him, smiled, and lowered her head again to her work. Irina was pouring beans on the floor. Father struck the table with his palm. "Yes," he shouted. "I *have* the patience of a saint." He glared at mother. Mother did not raise her head. That was too much for father. He rushed out of the room.

When father came back he was naked to the waist. He was carrying his shirt in his hand. To put his shirt on he sat down on the hearth bench. The light from the fire played on his naked body. He rubbed his hairy chest and arms briskly, put on his shirt, came to the table, and opened the paper. Cilly, the cat, jumped on the table and curled up in front of father. A moment later she was purring. Peace and quiet. A rubdown with snow had calmed father.

In the dead of winter I loved to listen to the wind singing under the eaves. Sometimes when it was very cold we would hear a sharp report as if a gun had been fired. Father would look up from the paper and say, "There is great cold tonight. The bark on the trees is bursting." Then he would turn to his paper. Mother would continue her handiwork and I felt happy in the warmth of our house.

My dreams were stimulated by stories Uncle Gherasim told us. I went out in fancy on adventures, one more exciting than the other, to return always to this heaven of peace where no danger could reach me. No dragon or fury could come into our house. Our doors were heavy, with large, wrought-iron hinges and heavy locks. The windows were protected by shutters as heavy as the doors. And then, there was father. What monster could stand up against him? Father was not afraid of anything.

It happened one early evening in the winter that Vasile Ungurean came to us. He was not entirely sober, a tall, bony, square-shouldered fellow, who had served four years in prison for killing a man. They were drinking in the inn, at Bucur's, Vasile and his victim. Father saw them as he went in and passed by their table into the small room where he always was served by the innkeeper. The two men greeted father. They seemed peaceful, two friends having a quiet talk over their spirits. But after a short time, when Bucur came into the room he said to father,

"Vasile is up to mischief. He grins and shows his teeth like a dog that bites stealthily. And he keeps filling Pantilimon's glass and poking him in the ribs with his elbow."

"They are friends," father said.

"They were the best of friends until four years ago when they had a quarrel and have never spoken to each other since. This is the first time they have come together. 'We made peace,' Vasile said as they entered the inn. 'Bucur, give us some of your best plum brandy.' Pantilimon merely nodded his head."

"So they are friends again," father said. Bucur shrugged his shoulders and left the room.

After some time father heard singing. Then a gruff voice shouted, "Louder! Raise the roof! Shake the windows! I am making peace with you!" The singer raised his voice. "Louder, louder," shouted the other voice.

Father opened the door. Vasile Ungurean was on his feet, standing threateningly over Pantilimon, who was straining his voice to sing louder.

Suddenly Vasile shouted, "I made you sing, you pig dog. I don't like your song, pig dog. I will silence you." With that he snatched out his knife and stabbed Pantilimon in the throat. It all happened in a flash.

Vasile swore he committed the act in self-defense, but father testified against him. Bucur said on the witness stand he did not see what happened. He was afraid to bear witness against Vasile, who was condemned to four years in prison on father's testimony.

The people in the village feared Vasile. He carried in his belt a bigger knife than the rest of the men.

We had heard his voice in the kitchen. "I want to see

your master," he said to Anica. Then suddenly the door opened and there he was in the room.

"How did you get in here?" father asked sharply.

"Through the door," Vasile said, grinning with one side of his mouth. His teeth showed.

The next instant father was on his feet, facing him within two steps. "Get out!" father said.

"I have to settle something with you," Vasile said. He reached to his belt. We never knew how it happened, but Vasile crashed to the floor with a groan. Father was standing over him. "Get up, you drunken pig," father shouted. Vasile groaned, "You burst my guts." But with more groaning he managed to get to his feet. He was very bent and holding his middle with both hands. Father slapped his face. Vasile staggered. Then he slapped his other cheek. Vasile groaned and gritted with his teeth. Again he made to pull his knife. Father grabbed a chair.

"In the name of God, Paul, don't," mother pleaded. Irina and I started to cry. It was mother's voice that made me cry.

Father did not strike Vasile with the chair, but he had it ready. "Out, drunken pig," he shouted. Vasile backed to the door. He fumbled for the latch with his left hand. His right hand was gripping the knife in his belt. He opened the door; then, with a terrible oath he snatched out the knife, plunged it into the door, and turned to run out. Father caught up with him at the kitchen door. He must have kicked him in the rear for we heard a heavy thud on the porch floor. Then we heard him begging, "Forgive, forgive, domnule." From father not a sound. Nicodin had to carry Vasile home. His only revenge was that he told everybody father was the devil himself. And we kept his knife. Nicodin refused to have it. "God forbid that I touch it. The knife of a murderer," he said. Father used it to whittle wooden swords for me. It was kept with the hammer and other tools in the woodshed. Mother would not have it in the house.

This incident convinced me that father could cope with any foe.

CHAPTER 27

೦೦೦೦೦೦೦೦೦೦೦೦

PEOPLE SAID THAT MOTHER HAD SO MUCH LOVE IN her heart she emanated it. Young women with child came to her, not so much for advice—that they could get from the midwife—but "to fill their hearts with love," they said. They never came with idle hands. They brought their distaffs or things to embroider. Mother gave Thursday afternoon to them.

That was a cheerful day. These young prospective mothers sang and worked and chatted and laughed and made themselves good blood. They sat in a half circle in our large room, facing mother in her big chair, her feet on a footstool.

Father used to say mother looked like a mother hen with her brood around her.

"If you had wings, Barbara, you would spread them over these fledglings," he said.

"They are lovely, dear," mother said. "Their hope makes them so."

"What hope, Barbara?"

"To have a beautiful child, dear. Every prospective mother hopes that," mother said.

The children in our village were beautiful, especially the girls. And father admitted that Ileana, One-eyed John's daughter, was a great beauty.

On these Thursdays I liked to sit by mother for an hour or so because it seemed like a holiday, although my vacations consisted of holidays only.

At this particular Christmas I had two Thursdays. And it was now that Paraschiva Luca, who had married Anton Luca in the spring, came with the other young women.

Paraschiva was the gayest of them all. She had no mother and had served three years in the city where she learned from her mistress how to cook German dishes. And she also had learned a German lullaby which she sang in her deep alto voice.

It was a pleasant enough lullaby, but all the young women said that they preferred the Romanian. And they sang in chorus several lullabies they had learned when they were children themselves, and which had come down "on the waves of time from a long forgotten past," they said.

"Like the song of the Miller's Daughter," Irina said. It was her favorite.

"Yes," Paraschiva said and she started to sing it. The other young women joined in the song. Soon they had tears in their eyes and Irina sobbed, so sad was this song.

But no sooner did they finish the song than Paraschiva started a hora and everybody clapped with her hands the tempo of the lively dance tune.

"You might dance then," mother said, laughing.

"As we are?" one of the young women said, blushing.

"She is in the seventh month," Maria Dornu said, "we excuse her." The others danced a little and this one merely clapped with her hands, all flushed.

It was on the second Thursday of my vacation when Popa Radu came while the dance was going on. We did not hear him knock on the door so he opened it wide and stood there in the frame, huge and beaming. The moment the dancers saw him they stopped, but Paraschiva went on singing.

Popa Radu greeted mother and stepped into the room. Now Paraschiva hushed, and all the young women went over to kiss his hand. He patted each one on the cheek and when the courtesy was over he said, "Now I will show you how to put hot coals under your feet." He threw off his sheepskin coat and said to Paraschiva, "Strike up, young woman."

"Yes, your reverence," Paraschiva said, and instantly started a sirba.

Popa Radu boomed out, "To the dance," and, like the enormous father of all the sprites he danced as if indeed there were hot coals under his feet. And although he had heavy boots on, he barely made any noise, so lightly did he hop about.

"This dance calls for stamping with the feet, but I did not want to shake the house and have your windows shattered," he said to mother when he stopped.

"Stay with us, reverence," mother invited Popa Radu. Paraschiva rushed up with father's big chair.

"Thank you, dear hostess," Popa Radu said, sitting down. He looked at the young women and beamed. "It is

265

like being in an orchard with young trees in bloom," he said. The young women lowered their heads, blushing, but they smiled.

"Ah!" Popa Radu said, heaving deeply. "Life is beautiful. And when I see it blooming, my heart swells with joy."

"Young women, may the good Lord bless the fruit you are bringing forth," he said.

"Thank you, reverend father, may the Lord hear you," the young women said in chorus.

The gossips said that regarding women Popa Radu had the eyes of a serpent. But mother said it was the abundance of life he was blessed with, nothing else.

"I came to see Paul," Popa Radu said to mother. "I knew your day for this gathering, but I wanted to greet you and bring you my wife's love." He rose. Mother saw him to the door, after the women had again kissed his hand and had their cheeks patted. "I leave you all in the peace of the Lord," he said, turning at the door to face the room.

Soon after Popa Radu left mother sent me out to play.

When I left for the city I thought that this Christmas holiday was the most beautiful and also the most eventful of all.

When I came home the following year for my summer vacation, I found mother as cheerful as ever. But her face was thinner and more pale than before. It is true that mother never had so much color as Irina or myself. Still, her increased pallor was noticeable to me, who had not seen her in nearly three months.

Also I noticed that Uncle Gherasim, on that first Sunday after my arrival, as he sat facing mother, would look

at her earnestly, then frown a little as one who was searching an answer to a puzzling question.

We both, Uncle Gherasim and myself, were very sensitive to any change in mother's appearance and to her
moods. What must have puzzled Uncle Gherasim was
mother's cheerfulness. She laughed heartily at the droll-
eries he and father told during and after our Sunday
supper.

Then one day, a week later, mother did not rise in the
morning at her accustomed time. It was one of those
beautiful early July mornings when one feels all of nature
expanding with life. From the fields of ripening wheat
came that rare fragrance of straw, baked earth, and the
wild red pea which mother said made of the world a
sacred temple because it had a fragrance as sweet as
myrrh, which was burned in our church on great holidays.

Mother's room was in the back of the house, three windows looking over the garden, to the west. She loved the
room because she could see the sun setting behind the
hill where the vineyards were. And in the morning she
could "open my eyes on the garden," as she put it, which
was lovely when abundant with living growth and also
when resting under a heavy blanket of snow.

I remember on a morning when the earth was white and
mother lifted me in her arms and showed me the garden,
saying, "You see, my little soul, the garden is covered now
and is sleeping." I was small, two years old perhaps, but
the impression of the snow-covered garden and mother's
words have remained undimmed in my mind.

But now it was summer and I was eleven years old and
had learned the Hungarian and German languages and
this was my happy yearly vacation. A long, long stretch

267

of days, games, boating in the mill canal, and walking home in bare feet, the warm dust of the street pushing between my toes as soft as carded wool.

It was the season when Uncle Gherasim went to bed early, but having heard from the neighbors that mother was unwell he came in the evening with a pot of new honey. For cover he put a large grape leaf on the pot. He asked if he could see mother. Father took him to her room, Irina and I following them.

"Good evening, good evening, my Mandra," Uncle Gherasim greeted. Mother, smiling, answered, "Welcome with God, Uncle Gherasim," and extended her hand.

"Now then, my Mandra, this is not proper to your nature. No, not at all," Uncle Gherasim said.

"It is nothing much, Uncle Gherasim. Tomorrow I shall be up again and you must come and have dinner with us. We shall have pancakes with plum jam," mother said.

"Now, that is good. Very good," Uncle Gherasim said. Then they spoke about his bees, about the grapes, the plums—the year was very good for this fruit—and when Anna brought in the lamp and lit it, Uncle Gherasim left.

Mother kissed Irina and me good night and we left the room too. Father took Uncle Gherasim to the gate; then he returned and went to mother, telling us to make ready for bed.

In the morning I went to mother. She was in bed, but her hair was freshly combed and braided and the braids, beautifully black and heavy, were on the pillow, one on each side of the head. She kissed me and said, "Good morning, my little soul, did you have beautiful dreams?" Since I had been very little mother always asked me this question.

268

I asked if she were getting up this day and she said no because father had asked her to stay in bed. "But tomorrow, my little soul, I shall be up," she said.

During the day I went several times to see mother. I always went in on tiptoes, although the door was ajar. When she was not dozing she read her favorite prayer book, the one bound in leather and the pages gilt edged. If she did not hear me enter she saw me when I was at the bed, and then she laid the book down and spoke to me. She seemed happy and peaceful and said she was feeling much better.

But mother was pale now excepting a faint flush of color high on her cheeks, and sometimes her forehead had tiny beads of sweat on it.

Uncle Gherasim came for dinner. We had pancakes with plum jam, roast lamb, and soup seasoned with green, unripe grapes, but mother did not sit with us at table and it was Anna who prepared the dinner and prepared the pancakes, with advice mother had been giving her.

Anna was a peasant girl. She had the most beautiful black eyes I had ever seen. They were beautiful when she was happy, and beautiful when suddenly tears welled out of them.

She had come to us two years before, brought by her father. She was seventeen then. They were from the neighboring village and her father knew us, having consulted father in some legal matter. He gave Anna over to mother with these words, "Doamna, my daughter is as good as warm bread, but she has a great pain in her heart. Her beloved was killed in the woods. He and a friend of his were felling a large, dead oak and the misfortune was fated to be his. The tree fell on him. I know you will be kind to her."

"Let your heart be at peace. Anna will be well with us," mother said. She taught Anna to cook and to do all the work in the house, and Anna learned quickly. She was a friend to Irina and me from the first day. When we called, "Anna," she always answered, "Dear," and when mother called her she answered, *Porunciti,* which means "Command me." She was now like a member of the family, but, with the innate peasant reserve, strictly kept her place.

She served at the table this evening as she had done before, but she glanced at mother's empty chair and her eyes were sad. I noticed it and became sad too. I was always influenced by the mood of a person I loved.

Uncle Gherasim sat at table leisurely. They spoke about one thing or another and laughed too. I took heart and said to myself, Tomorrow she will be with us at table again. And when dinner was over I went into the kitchen to Anna.

Nicodin was there. He had finished his supper and sat on the stool by the hearth, smoking his pipe.

We all liked Nicodin. I could say I loved him, for Nicodin was as kind as he was clever at work, especially with animals. He knew everything about horses, oxen, cows, goats, sheep, and even fowls. And his voice was deep and warm like father's. He knew many, many folk songs and sang them in a subdued voice that sounded as if it came from afar, "like a sweet, gentle breeze," Anna used to say with tears in her eyes, though she smiled listening to him.

270

"Come and sit by me," Nicodin said as I entered the kitchen. He smelled of the stable. It was not the smell of manure, but the sweet odor of oxen and horses and hay, which I like more, even, than the fragrance of wood smoke in the crisp autumn air.

"So, Peter, you are going to be a man of book learning when you grow up," he said. "Do you like your city school?"

"I like the school but I will be a farmer," I said.

Nicodin chuckled. "And all the book learning, Peter, what will become of that? It will not help you at chopping wood," he said. He felt my arms.

"I will be strong," I said, leaving the question about book learning unanswered because I did not know the answer.

"Certainly you will be strong," Nicodin said assuringly, and he felt my arms again. Anna came to the hearth to fetch hot water for dishwashing. She bent down and kissed me on top of my head. "He will be a good and brave young man," she said to Nicodin.

"May the Lord hear you," Nicodin said. It was not with doubt and a sigh he said these words, as sometimes old women did when they were not certain that the Lord would grant a request or fulfill a wish. Nicodin spoke with fervor.

The sun was setting behind the vineyard's hill and we heard the cowherd crack his whip and blow his horn.

"I must open the gate for our cows," Nicodin said. I went out with him.

Like the buffalo cow, our cow, Balana, was never the first in the herd. She was a large, mild animal, and took her time always. The head of the herd had already passed

271

our gate when Nicodin opened it. I watched the cows, the dust they raised with their cloven hoofs, and smelled the odor of their warm bodies. Balana and our buffalo cow were quite the last of the herd. She came toward the gate, stopped, looked at us, then leisurely walked in, straight to the water trough by the well. Very deliberately and flipping her ears, the buffalo cow came in. She also went to the trough and plunged her black muzzle into the water.

I put my hand on Balana's throat and felt the water go down it as if it were balls she was swallowing. I dared not go too near the buffalo cow. Not that she was nasty, but she was terribly black and the expression in her eyes was distant, not friendly like Balana's.

Nicodin closed the gate and while I watched the cows drink he went to the kitchen door and asked Anna for the milk pails.

Near the water trough was a short, thick piece of log. Nicodin used it as a stool for milking the cows, but when he milked the two goats he sat on the ground, with the pail between his legs. Our goats had so much milk that it sprinkled to right and to left from their large teats as they walked in from the back of the plum orchard where they pastured all day. Nicodin had their front legs tied so they could not jump and damage the trees.

After Nicodin took in the milk for Anna to strain and put in the cellar, we sat together on a bench against the barn wall. In the cool of the evening the warm wall which had the sun on it all day felt good against my back. And it was good to be near Nicodin. Just sitting by him and listening to him, I felt much as I did when I was convalesc-

272

ing and my strength grew daily. He had something about him of the permanence and solidity of the hills. The only difference was that the hills changed in aspect with the seasons; Nicodin was ever the same. He was ever summer in nature. The sun was within him.

On this evening Nicodin spoke little. He smoked his pipe in silence. When the kitchen windows shone from the kerosene lamp that hangs from the ceiling, Nicodin rose.

"Good night, Peter. Sleep is calling me," he said, patting my shoulder. He emptied the last ashes from his pipe, stamped his foot on them, and walked to the barn where he slept in the hay. I went into the house.

Every morning Irina and I went in to see mother. Always I asked mother if she felt better, and invariably her answer was, "Yes, my little soul, I feel better." But the days passed and mother remained in bed. Old Suzanna, who inherited all the medicinal herbs from Anghelina and a good part of her knowledge too, came to us daily. She brewed teas from various blossoms and leaves, and rubbed mother's feet with salves, much to father's annoyance. Mother drank the teas and submitted gently and good-naturedly to the old woman's treatment. Suzanna murmured a prayer when she massaged mother's feet and said, when she offered her infusions, "Drink this good medicine, in the name of the Father, the Son, and the Holy Ghost, to your good health, Amen." And every morning when I asked mother if she felt better she said, "Yes, my little soul, I feel better." But she remained in bed.

Several physicians came. They prescribed, one this, one

273

that, prescriptions in Latin that father tried to make out, and mother took those medicines as cheerfully as she drank the infusions prepared by old Suzanna.

Then, one day Uncle Andrei, who had a reputation as a doctor, brought Dr. Kuh, a great physician from Budapest. Dr. Kuh was a small stocky man with heavy eyebrows and very piercing gray eyes. His hands were large, but soft as silk cushions.

They stayed a long time in mother's room. When they left, father saw them to the carriage. Dr. Kuh spoke to father before he took his seat in the carriage and then, leaning out and holding father's hand, he spoke more, father merely nodding. Irina and I watched from the porch.

When the carriage pulled out from the yard, father stood there for a long moment. When he came, he patted us, Irina and me, on the cheeks and went into the house, saying not a word. In the evening Uncle Gherasim came. Soon Popa Ivan and his wife arrived. They came from Sibiu where Popa Ivan had his church. They were old friends of ours.

Popa Ivan was tall and thin, with a black beard and long, black locks. But his wife, Priestess Arghira the peasants called her, was plump and fair and very vivacious. It was she who had brought about Popa Ivan's promotion from a village church to a church in Sibiu and, the gossips said, "if she preserves her fair looks and vivacity long enough she will make a bishop of him."

She started at once to hold forth against doctors and made fun of the celebrated Kuh. "With a name like that," she said, laughing, "a stump of a man, I saw him, it is a wonder how he won such a reputation." Kuh in German is cow.

"Of course Andrei is different," she said to father, smiling. "He is a man and handsome. When he feels your pulse, well, you know the man is all there with everything he knows. But we are people of faith. There is no greater healer than faith. Men have their place," she glanced at her husband, who was toying with the silver chain on which hung a silver cross, his eyes lowered, "but faith has the good Lord in it, like day has the sun."

She spoke at length about faith and the boundless goodness of God. Then she gave father a small book. "This will do more good than all the doctors in the world," she said.

"The Dream of the Virgin Mary, Mother of our Savior, Jesus Christ," father read the title.

"It is indeed," Priestess Arghira said reverently. "Now," she continued, "if someone should repeat the words in the book, every one of them, with faith, at the patient's bedside, every morning, the good Lord will restore her health."

"The Lord is merciful," Popa Ivan said solemnly.

Father thanked Priestess Arghira and said we should have the book read for mother.

"That is very good," Priestess Arghira said. And then she turned to me, her face glowing with kindness. "I think," she said, "Peter should read it. The sweet, innocent soul." She drew me to her and kissed me on both cheeks.

"I will, father," I said. "Please allow me, father." And tears burned in my eyes.

"Certainly, Peter, you may," father said.

"The Lord's power and goodness are beyond comprehension," Popa Ivan said.

"Boundless," Priestess Arghira said.

"Boundless, indeed," asserted Popa Ivan.

I was happy and proud too, although I felt that pride was unbecoming, but it was my sister who brought it out in me. She looked at me as if to say, "You do not deserve it." And she was pouting as always when she resented something.

One never knew what would bring out contrary feelings in Irina. She had a heart of gold, people said, for she would give away her last penny to a friend whom she loved, and to a beggar she always gave something besides a very large slice of bread. A piece of cold meat, ham or bacon or an egg. But she had her unaccountable moods and this pouting of which nothing could cure her.

"Look at you," mother would say. "Your face is all puckered up, dear. You really look like a stormy day."

At such times Irina would blush terribly, but her face remained unchanged otherwise. Father would merely glance at her, his one eyebrow raised, and push out his mustaches as a sort of masculine yet futile challenge.

Now, when father allowed us to leave the table, I went at once to the kitchen, carrying the little book with me. Irina followed me. At the kitchen door she pushed me aside and entered ahead of me. She assumed a very haughty air, strode to the table and sat down on the bench.

Anna, at the end of the table, was mending some linen apparel. "Come, dears," she said, and stopped her handiwork for the moment.

276

Nicodin had gone to his bed in the hayloft.

"And what is the little book, dear?" Anna asked me.

Irina compressed her lips and pushed out her chin defiantly. I blushed to the roots of my hair, but said, "Priestess Arghira gave it to me. I will read it every morning until mother gets well. She will get well."

Suddenly Irina burst into tears, jumped up and ran out of the kitchen. Anna called to her, but Irina slammed the door, a thing she should not have done. Slamming doors was a great misdeed in our house.

"And what book is it, dear?" Anna asked, leaning over to me. I told her. Then I read the preface to the dream. Anna listened attentively, resting from her sewing. I read that whoever repeats the sacred words of Virgin Mary's Dream must never allow his mind to wander from the spirit of the text, for then the prayer will not be accepted. It also said that should it be so decreed by the Lord that the patient for whom the prayer is offered shall be taken from this earthly life, the prayers will guide his soul into paradise.

"But mother will not be taken away. She will get well," I said, overcome by anxiety.

"Of course she will, dear," Anna said, but already her eyes were full of tears.

"Then why do you cry?" I asked.

"I am not crying, dear, no, no! See?" Anna said. She smiled, took me in her arms and held me for a long moment. And then she said, "Now, dear, go to sleep and in the morning say the good prayer. I pray too, every evening, for your dear mother's health. From now on I will pray in the morning too, while I make the fire." She kissed me and I went to my room.

Actually it was not my room, it was our room, Irina's and mine. And now, since she considered herself grown up, my only share in the room was about one quarter of it, where my bed stood, and a small table. Yes, and a chair too. When Irina made ready for bed she placed a screen that hid her bed and table from my part of the room. We were not allowed to read in bed, by candle light, but we could light our respective candles while we undressed because the ceiling lamp was put out. That was Irina's task. Nevertheless, after my candle was out Irina's was still burning, but I never knew how long for I always fell asleep the moment I was well nestled in bed.

In the morning mother received me with her usual smile and said she was feeling better. But her hand was hot and moist. I told her about the prayer.

"Oh, my dear little soul!" she said. "Now I certainly will get well very soon."

I knelt down at the side of the bed and began to read. I put all my attention into what I read, but before I got to the fourth page I suddenly found myself thinking of the boys whose voices I heard in the street. Three times I had to start from the beginning before I could get through with the forty-seven pages without my mind wandering, though I was not absolutely certain about it. My knees hurt terribly when I got up. Mother was slumbering. I walked out on tiptoe. That day I played and bathed with my friends in the mill canal, very happy because I had done my duty.

Uncle Andrei came once a week now to see that the instructions of Dr. Kuh were followed and to replenish the medicines in time. It was father who gave the medicines to mother, three times a day. If Uncle Andrei was present he counted the drops himself as father let them fall into the half glass of water from an oat straw which he very carefully dipped in the medicine bottle. Later, Uncle Andrei brought an eyedropper.

Every morning mother told me she was feeling better, but the days came and passed and she remained in bed. Now I knew the entire booklet by heart but dared not repeat the prayer without reading it for fear of missing a word. Nor could I ever go from beginning to end without being diverted from the sacred text at least twice. Some days I would be almost at the last page, when suddenly the call of some boy or girl would intrude upon me and take my mind away. But now I knelt on a small cushion, which mother made me do, and that was a great help.

Everybody, and especially Anna and Nicodin, were sure that mother would get well. They both had great faith in the prayer that I had read to them and even repeated once or twice without the book. When I said amen they both crossed themselves saying, "May the Lord hear you."

Forty-six days I repeated the prayer at mother's bedside. In the morning of the forty-seventh day, when I came into mother's room, father was there and Popa Ivan.

Mother was breathing very heavily. Popa Ivan adjusted his peplum and opened a book. Father had a lighted candle in his hand.

"Put the candle in her hand," Popa Ivan said to father.

Mother could not hold the candle. Father held her hand, into which he had placed it. He turned to me and

279

said in a whisper, "Go to your sister, son." I held up the book, signifying that I came to say the prayer. "Do it in the next room," father whispered.

As I closed the door I heard Popa Ivan's voice in a sing-song. In the yard the hens were cackling. A wagon was passing by the house. It rumbled heavily and the peasant was calling to the oxen. I imagined a very heavy load on the wagon, the oxen straining in the yoke. I could see the street, the yard with the fowls in it, the garden and the plum orchard where the fruit was nearly ripe in the early variety, everything as in the other summers. All was very vivid in my imagination as I sat in the corner of the room looking into space.

Then suddenly I realized that this summer was different from all the others. I must kneel down by the icon and repeat the Dream of the Virgin Mary, Mother of Our Savior, Jesus Christ.

I had read eight pages when the small church bells began to toll. At once my mind roved. I started again from the first page, but before I turned it father and Popa Ivan came into the room.

"Where is your sister, son?" father asked. He lifted me to my feet and pressed me to him. He was heaving from the effort to stifle his weeping. Holding me pressed to him, he said, "Your dear mother has left us, son."

"May the good Lord rest her soul in eternal peace," Popa Ivan said. He put his hand on my head. "You are a good boy. Your mother's soul is in Paradise. Have you heard the tolling of the small bells? An innocent child has given its soul to God this morning. The gates of Heaven were open when your dear mother's soul left this earthly life."

280

"Thank his reverence, son," father said.

"Thank you, your reverence," I said, and I kissed Popa Ivan's hand. Then I broke into sobbing.

"Son, son!" father said, straining me to him.

When Irina and I were taken in to see mother, the church bells were tolling. The big bells. For mother. She looked beautiful, sleeping peacefully.

In the yard and in the street the noises were as they had been in all other summers I had known. But this was a great and very sad day. And the sadness of the day cast a pall of sadness over this summer.